Challenger SECOND EDITION 3

ADULT READING SERIES

Corea Murphy

New Readers Press

Images courtesy of:
p. 6, p. 11, p. 16, p. 21, p. 22, p. 27, p. 28, p. 32, p. 33, p. 37, p. 38, p. 42, p. 43, p. 50, p. 51, p. 55, p. 61, p. 62, p. 74, p. 75, p. 79, p. 80, p. 85, p. 90, p. 91, p. 98, p. 99, p. 103, p. 104, p. 108, p. 109, p. 114 © 2008 Jupiterimages Corporation; p. 7, p. 66, p. 84, p. 115: istockphoto.com

Challenger 3, 2nd Edition
ISBN 978-1-56420-570-4

Copyright © 2010 New Readers Press
New Readers Press
ProLiteracy's Publishing Division
104 Marcellus Street, Syracuse, New York 13204
www.newreaderspress.com

Printed in the United States of America
9   8

Proceeds from the sale of New Readers Press materials support professional development, training, and technical assistance programs of ProLiteracy that benefit local literacy programs in the U.S. and around the globe.

Developmental Editor: Terrie Lipke
Contributing Writer: Nina Shope
Creative Director: Andrea Woodbury
Production Specialist: Maryellen Casey
Art and Design Supervisor: James P. Wallace
Cover Design: Carolyn Wallace

Table of Contents

Review of Long and Short Vowels

ā	ē	ī	ō	ū
ape	eve	vine	owe	Luke
gale	deep	ivy	dome	reduce
gaze	she's	wise	dose	Ruth
pave	she'd	wisely	mope	confuse
vane	Steven	firelight	cove	true
ă	ĕ	ĭ	ŏ	ŭ
ad	hem	bin	ox	buzz
Sam	jet	chin	job	cuff
van	Ted	kin	socks	hush
raft	tense	sift	knot	rut
pact	dense	rinse	rotten	putty

Words for Study

Carpenter besides they're weight
visits already exercise we'll
window advice YMCA how's

Steven Takes Some Advice

Steven Carpenter had been driving a van for five years. He liked his job very much, but sometimes the long hours of driving made him feel tense.

Every Thursday night, Steven dropped by his older sister's house for dinner. His sister's name was Ruth. During one of these weekly visits, Ruth watched her brother gaze out the living-room window as she rinsed the dirty dinner dishes.

"You're not going to mope around all night again, are you?" asked Ruth.

"Sorry," answered Steven. "I had to drive two hundred and seventy miles over badly paved roads today. I'm so tensed up that I really feel rotten. Maybe I'll go home and try to get a good night's sleep."

"You know, Steve," said Ruth, "you really owe it to yourself to do something besides working all the time. You're still young, but you're already getting into a rut. You should go out more, do things, meet some new people."

Steven wisely kept his mouth shut. There was no point in trying to stop Ruth once she made up her mind to give him advice.

"Look at this," said Ruth, pointing to an ad in the evening paper. "They're starting an exercise class down at the YMCA. This is just what you need to feel more relaxed."

"Who needs exercise?" Steven said loudly. He was beginning to lose his temper. "I'm as strong as an ox. You're the one who needs to lose weight. You go!"

"You don't have to lose your temper just because I'm trying to help you!" Ruth shouted back. "Anyway, this would be a very good way to meet some new people."

Steven said nothing.

At last, Ruth said, "Look, we'll make a pact. You go to the exercise class for six weeks, and I'll try to mind my own business. How's that?"

Steven grinned, "I know you won't be able to keep that pact." As he rose from the couch to get himself another cup of coffee, his whole body felt sore. "You know something?" said Steven. "You're right. I do need exercise. Let me see that ad again."

1 About the Story. Answer these questions.

1. What does Steven Carpenter do for a living? _driving a van_

2. How long has Steven had this job? _For Five years._

3. What is the name of Steven's sister? _Ruth_

4. How often does Steven see his sister? _Every Thursday night Steven go_
Pass his sister house For dinner

5. List two reasons why the sister thinks an exercise class would be good for Steven.

   a. _exercise class will be good For Steven to take his mind_
   OFF oF things

   b. _____

6. How does Steven react to his sister's advice at first?
   temper

7. What does Steven decide to do at the end of the story?
   take advice

8. Based on how the word is used in this story, what do you think a *pact* is?
   a agrement

What do you think?

9. Do you think the sister's life is in a rut? (Sentences in this story will help you answer this question.) _No I think the sister to busy worrying about her brother._

10. How old do you think Steven is? (Sentences in this story will help you answer this question.)
I know he are young so I'm give to say around 26 of age

2 The Ending -ing. Add -ing to these words. Study the examples before you begin.

1. bless __**blessing**__
2. build __building__
3. clear __clearing__

4. dress __dressing__
5. stuff __stuffing__
6. wash __washing__

1. bathe __**bathing**__
2. line __lining__
3. pave __paving__

4. confuse __confusing__
5. come __coming__
6. ice __Icing__

1. bed __**bedding**__
2. knot __Knotting__
3. fit __Fitting__

4. cut __cutting__
5. pad __padding__
6. wed __wedding__

3 How Do These People Earn a Living? Match each word below with the sentence that best describes the job.

baker	dishwasher	farmer	miner	teller
coach	driver	lawyer	teacher	waiter

teacher 1. This person helps people with their work in school and grades papers.

baker 2. This person makes pies, rolls, bread, and other good things to eat.

Farmer 3. This person plants crops in the spring and mends tools and fences in the winter.

driver 4. This person drives a truck or van full of goods from place to place.

miner 5. This person seeks gold or brings coal up from under the ground.

waiter 6. This person takes people's orders and hopes for big tips.

coach 7. This person helps a team win games.

dishwasher 8. This person cleans the dishes in a restaurant.

teller 9. This person works in a bank and cashes people's paychecks.

lawyer 10. When people are sued, they hire this person to go to court with them.

4 Compound Words. Find the two little words in each compound word, and put them on the lines to the right.

1. roadwork _____ + _____
2. sidewalk _____ + _____
3. toolbox _____ + _____
4. grapevine _____ + _____
5. backfire _____ + _____

6. dishpan _____ + _____
7. pigpen _____ + _____
8. mankind _____ + _____
9. homemade _____ + _____
10. newspaper _____ + _____

Review of Consonant Blends and Digraphs: Part 1

ch		sh		st	
chalk	bench	shade	clash	stem	beast
cheat	perch	shark	gosh	stew	breast
chore	porch	shelf	leash	stir	cost
chose	pinch	shook	mash	stone	feast
chow	starch	shorts	rash	stool	mist
chunk	stitch	shove	stash	stunt	paste

Words for Study

Jerome	kitchen	pretty	probably
lowered	wandered	lessons	afford
yoga	difference	entered	splurge

Meet Jerome

Steven, who had only his shirt and shorts on, was standing on his head in the middle of his bedroom. His eyes were closed, and his face had a very peaceful look.

"That's a great stunt," said his friend, Jerome, as he walked into the room. "Where did you learn that?"

"It's not a stunt," answered Steven calmly as he lowered himself to the floor. "This is yoga."

By now Jerome was perched on a stool in the kitchen. He was feasting on some beef stew that Steven had made for dinner. "When did you start doing yoga?" shouted Jerome.

"Last Tuesday," answered Steven. "I went down to the YMCA to sign up for an exercise class, and I wandered into the yoga class by mistake."

Jerome was confused. "What's the difference between yoga class and exercise class?" he shouted. "If you ask me, it just looks like yoga means you do stranger exercises."

"I guess it does look pretty strange," said Steven. "I'm not sure what the difference is. I missed the talk at the beginning of class. Since it only costs thirty dollars for ten lessons, I decided to give it a try."

Jerome shook his head slowly. "What's the matter?" asked Steven as he entered the kitchen. "You probably think I'm crazy for doing this, don't you?" Jerome was Steven's best friend, and he cared very much what Jerome thought about what he did.

"No, I don't think you're crazy," said Jerome. "I just think this is the worst stew I've ever had in my life. It tastes like paste! As long as you're making all these great changes, why don't you learn how to cook?"

"Very funny," said Steven. "Come on, just give me a few minutes to get dressed, and I'll treat you to a steak dinner." Steven really couldn't afford to go around buying steak dinners. But he was so glad that Jerome hadn't laughed at him for taking the yoga class that he decided to splurge.

1 About the Story. Answer these questions.

1. What is the name of Steven's best friend? _Jerome_

2. What class is Steven taking at the YMCA? _yoga class_

3. How did Steven happen to take this class instead of the one he had planned to take?
Steven walk into the yoga class by misake

4. What does Jerome think the difference is between exercise class and yoga?
Stranger exercise

5. Why does Steven want to treat his friend to a steak dinner?
Because He didn't make him Feel bad

6. What clues in this story tell you Jerome has visited Steven before?
He just walk in

2 Adding -est to Words. Study the examples. Then add -est to the words.

1. fine + est = **finest**

2. rude + est = _rudest_

3. nice + est = _nicest_

4. late + est = _latest_

5. ripe + est = _ripest_

6. sore + est = _sorest_

1. proud + est = **proudest**

2. short + est = _shortest_

3. cheap + est = _cheapest_

4. great + est = _greatest_

5. mean + est = _meanest_

6. high + est = _highest_

1. sad + est = **saddest**
2. big + est = bigest
3. thin + est = thinest

4. dim + est = dimest
5. mad + est = madest
6. hot + est = hotest

3 How Do These People Earn a Living? Match each word below with the sentence that best describes the job.

| actor | bodyguard | clown | fisherman | scribe | tailor |
| babysitter | carpenter | doctor | reporter | shortstop | trainer |

reporter — **1.** This person asks questions to get the news.

carpenter — **2.** This person builds and fixes things that are made out of wood.

bodyguard — **3.** This person is hired to guard someone's life.

actor — **4.** This person learns lines for roles in movies and plays.

tailor — **5.** This person makes clothes and mends rips and tears.

babysitter — **6.** This person is hired to look after children.

trainer — **7.** This person helps people to get in shape.

clown — **8.** This person wears funny clothes and makes people laugh.

shortstop — **9.** This person plays on a baseball field.

fisherman — **10.** This person spends the day on a boat with poles and nets.

scribe — **11.** In the old days, when most people couldn't write, this person was hired to write letters.

doctor — **12.** You go to this person when you're feeling ill.

4 Compound Words. Find the two little words in each compound word, and put them on the lines to the right.

1. paycheck   pay   +   chect
2. toothpaste   tooth   +   paste
3. understand   under   +   stand
4. lampshade   lamp   +   shade
5. chalkboard   chalk   +   board
6. shortcake   short   +   cake
7. classroom   class   +   room
8. undershirt   under   +   shirt
9. flashlight   flash   +   light
10. cookbook   cook   +   book
11. workshop   work   +   shop
12. handshake   hand   +   shake

Review of Consonant Blends: Part 2

bl	br	cl	cr	fl	fr
blade	brace	clam	cramp	flap	frown
blank	bracelet	clench	crate	flail	fright
blast	branch	clerk	crow	flight	frame
blond	bribe	clung	crick	flip	frog
blindly	broil	clumsy	crude	flirt	frozen
bloom	brush	clutter	crutch	flute	fruit

Words for Study

subject	aside	shoulder	supposed
appeared	figure	frightened	website
balance	muscles	pose	scrolled

Jerome Learns About Yoga

The real reason Jerome hadn't said very much to Steven about the yoga class was that he wanted to wait until he knew more about yoga. The next day, Jerome did an Internet search on the subject and came up with a list of links.

He clicked on one of the links, and a picture appeared on the screen. The picture showed a blond woman who looked like she was twisted into a knot. Jerome cracked a smile. He couldn't picture his friend doing anything close to that. Steven was too clumsy. He'd break a limb and end up on crutches!

Then Jerome thought back to the other day. Steven had been standing on his head, and he hadn't lost his balance once. "It must be easier than it looks," Jerome thought.

He got up from his desk and cleared a spot on the floor. His room was crowded with clutter. Dust and crumbs clung to the floor. Jerome brushed them aside and cleaned a space for himself.

He crouched down in front of the wall and tried to figure out how to stand on his head. He braced his hands on the floor and clenched his muscles. Then he tried to flip his feet up in the air. For a minute, he thought it was going to work. Then he felt his shoulder blades cramp and his wrists give out. He came crashing down, right on the crown of his head. He heard a crack and felt a blast of pain. Jerome crawled blindly over to his desk, frightened that he had badly hurt himself. But the pain went away after he took a few deep breaths.

"Okay, maybe yoga isn't that easy," he said to himself, rubbing the crick in his neck. "That pose is supposed to clear your brain. But all I did was clear up some floor space in here!"

Jerome sat down and tried not to frown. He never had thought of himself as clumsy. He blushed as he pictured himself flailing around and falling flat on the floor. What a flop!

Yoga must be hard. Maybe that was why the website had so many books for sale. Jerome scrolled past a picture of people in some poses and read a bit of what was written below. The website claimed that yoga helped people work on their balance.

"I guess I could use some help with that myself," Jerome thought. He clicked the link to order a book.

1 About the Story. Answer these questions.

1. How does Jerome use the Internet to learn more about yoga?

   He came up with a list of links

2. Why does Jerome think Steven will be bad at yoga?

   He was too clumsy

3. What does Jerome think will happen if Steven tries yoga?

   He'd break a limb end up on crutches

4. What makes Jerome wonder if he is wrong about Steven?

   _____

5. Why does Jerome decide to try standing on his head?

   _____

6. Do you think Jerome cleans his room often? Why or why not?

   _____

7. Based on how the word is used in this story, what do you think *flail* means?

   _____

8. Why does Jerome decide yoga is hard?

   _____

9. In one sentence, tell what happens in this story.

   _____

2 Adding -y to Words. Study the examples. Then add -y to the words.

1. taste + y = __tasty__

2. shake + y = _____

3. shade + y = _____

4. stone + y = _____

5. edge + y = _____

1. flight + y = __flighty__

2. stuff + y = _____

3. cling + y = _____

4. rain + y = _____

5. leak + y = _____

1. run + y = __runny__

2. dog + y = _____

3. pat + y = _____

4. knot + y = _____

5. clam + y = _____

3 Who Uses What? Choose the best word below to fill in the blank for each sentence.

brain	computer	map	mower	proof	tent
brakes	jokes	mitt	oven	spell	words

1. A cook uses an _____ to bake a cake.

2. A thinker uses her _____ to fix a problem.

3. A camper uses a _____ to sleep in the woods.

4. A driver uses the _____ to stop the car.

5. A farmer uses a _____ to cut the grass.

6. A stranger uses a _____ to find his way around.

7. A catcher uses a _____ to catch a baseball.

8. A witch uses a _____ to turn a person into a frog.

9. A worker uses a _____ to find things on the Internet.

10. A writer uses _____ to tell a story.

11. A clown uses _____ to make people laugh.

12. A lawyer uses _____ to win a case.

4 Compound Words. Find the two little words in each compound word and put them on the lines to the right.

1. blackboard _____ + _____

2. earring _____ + _____

3. milkshake _____ + _____

4. fruitcake _____ + _____

5. overgrown _____ + _____

6. hairbrush _____ + _____

7. sunlight _____ + _____

8. suitcase _____ + _____

9. eyestrain _____ + _____

10. snowball _____ + _____

11. racecourse _____ + _____

12. freeway _____ + _____

Review of Consonant Blends: Part 3

gl	gr	pl	pr	sl	str
glance	grace	plainly	praise	sled	strain
globe	grouch	plead	press	sleet	stray
gloom	grouchy	pledge	prince	slept	streak
gloomy	grumpy	plenty	prop	slid	stress
glove	grief	plow	proper	slouch	stressful
glumly	grudge	plump	pry	slump	stretch

Words for Study

Mansfield	control	you've
fallen	improve	you'll
headache	complained	bother

Ginger Is Grumpy

Jerome called his girlfriend, Ginger Mansfield, on her cell phone. She picked up after a few rings, but she sounded grumpy.

"What do you want, Jerome?" Ginger snapped. "I was trying to sleep!"

"Don't be such a grouch," Jerome said. "I know you are stressed out, but you don't have to take it out on me."

"I'm sorry," Ginger said glumly. "I didn't mean to be rude. But I haven't slept well in days, and I strained my voice pretty badly the other night."

"You know what you should try? Yoga," Jerome said.

Ginger laughed. "Jerome, what do you know about yoga? I mean, when is the last time you even exercised?"

Now it was Jerome's turn to feel grouchy.

"I know plenty, Ginger," Jerome snapped. "Yoga would help you sleep better and feel less stressed out. I tried it just the other day." He didn't tell Ginger that he had fallen on his head, which had been a little stressful. Plus, he hadn't been able to sleep well because of his headache. "Yoga is good for the mind and the body, and it might help you control your mean streak, by the way. It might improve your slouch and give you a little more grace, too."

"That's really funny, Jerome, really funny." How on earth, thought Ginger, could she be in love with such a jerk? "Look, Jerome, are you coming over tonight or not?"

"I always come over to your place," complained Jerome. "Why don't you come over here for a change?"

"Because your place looks like a pigpen," Ginger answered. "It's full of clutter and dust, and you never clean up after yourself."

"You don't know what you are talking about," Jerome said. "I cleaned up the other day, right before I exercised. You know, you sound like you've got some kind of grudge against me!"

That was the last straw for Ginger. "Jerome, I don't need any more stress. I told you I was tired. Why are you giving me grief! Just tell me, are you coming over tonight or not?" she screamed.

"Stop screaming!" Jerome shouted. "You'll strain your voice!"

"I'm not screaming!" screamed Ginger.

"Well, this has been a great phone call," Jerome said. "Look, why don't you go do some yoga and calm down a bit, and I'll call back when I can hear again."

"Don't bother!" Ginger shouted, hanging up the phone.

1 About the Story. Answer these questions.

1. What is Ginger doing when Jerome calls her up? _Sleeping_

2. Why does Jerome tell Ginger she should take yoga classes? _____
To help with her stressed

3. Why does Jerome get grouchy with Ginger? _____
Because she screaming at him

4. Why doesn't Jerome want to go to Ginger's place? _____
Because she Never come over his home for a change

5. Give two reasons why Ginger doesn't want to go over to Jerome's place.
   a. _She doesn't want to go because his house clutte and dust_
   b. _And never clean up after hisself_

6. How does the phone call end? _Becouse she_

What do you think?

7. Do you think Ginger is going to make up with Jerome soon? Why or why not?
Yes I do because she Love him

2 Changing the y to i. Study how the first set has been done. Then do the same with the remaining words.

1. grouchy   **grouchier**   **grouchiest**

2. rainy   rainier   rainiest

3. icy   icier   iciest

4. stuffy   stuffier   stuffiest

5. stretchy   stretchier   stretchiest

6. rosy   rosier   rosiest

3 More Work with the Ending -y. Study the example. Then add -y to the ten words below. Match these words with the right sentences.

chill + y = **chilly**   blood + y = bloody

hair + y = hairy   jump + y = jumpy

risk + y = risky   salt + y = salty

brain + y = brainy   trick + y = tricky

puff + y = puffy   greed + y = greedy

1. A man who needs a shave has a hairy face.

2. A person who is very scared is often jumpy.

3. Ginger's eyes were puffy after crying so hard.

4. Driving a scooter without a helmet can be risky.

5. The night was so **chilly** that Ginger put on a hat and gloves.

6. Luke was so _____ that he never had to study for a test.

7. Soup from a can is sometimes very salty.

8. Some people don't like scary movies because of the _____ deaths.

9. The math problems seemed so tricky that Mary asked her aunt to help her with them.

10. People who want lots of money can be very _____.

4 Who Uses What? Choose the best word below to fill in the blank for each sentence.

brace	gloves	leash	prop	sled
globe	iron	plow	putty	spices

1. Ruth used an _____ to press the gown she planned to wear to the party.

2. Ted used a _____ when he took his dog for a walk.

3. The cook used _____ to make the stew more tasty.

4. The farmer used a _____ to get the field ready for planting.

5. The children used a _____ to go down the snowy hill.

6. The carpenter used some _____ to fix the window.

7. The teacher used a _____ to show the class where England is.

8. Luke used _____ to keep his hands warm.

9. The actor used a _____ gun in the stage shootout.

10. The doctor used a _____ to fix Ginger's slouch.

5 Compound Words. Find the two little words in each compound word, and write them on the lines to the right.

1. railroad _____ + _____

2. basketball _____ + _____

3. underground _____ + _____

4. grandmother _____ + _____

5. dreamland _____ + _____

6. grandfather _____ + _____

7. cheapskate _____ + _____

8. sleepover _____ + _____

Word Index: Lessons 1-4

A
actor
advice
afford
already
ape
appear
aside

B
backfire
balance
bathing
beast
bedding
beginning
bench
besides
bin
blackboard
blade
blank
blast
blend
blessing
blindly
blond
bloody
bloom
bother
brace
bracelet
brainy
branch
breast
bribe
broil
brush
building
buzz

C
camper
carpenter
chalk
chalkboard
cheapskate
cheat

chilly
chin
chore
chose
chow
chunk
clam
clammy
clash
clearing
clench
clerk
cling
clingy
clumsy
clung
clutter
coming
complain
confuse
confusing
control
cove
cramp
crate
crick
crow
crude
crutch
cuff
cutting

D
dense
difference
dishpan
dishwasher
doggy
dome
dose
dreamland
dressing

E
earring
edge
edgy
enter

eve
exercise
eyestrain

F
fallen
feast
figure
firelight
fisherman
fitting
flail
flap
flashlight
flight
flighty
flirt
flute
freeway
fright
frighten
frog
frown
frozen

G
gale
gaze
glance
globe
gloom
gloomy
glove
glumly
gosh
grace
grandfather
grandmother
grapevine
greedy
grief
grouchy
grudge
grumpy

H
hairbrush
hairy

handshake
headache
hem
homemade
how's
hush

I
icing
improve
iron
ivy

J
Jerome
jet
jumpy

K
kin
kitchen
knotting
knotty

L
lampshade
lawyer
leaky
leash
lesson
lining
lower
Luke

M
mankind
Mansfield
mash
milkshake
mist
mope
muscle

N
newspaper

O
overgrown
owe
ox

P
pact
padding
paste
patty
pave
paving
perch
pigpen
pinch
plainly
plead
pledge
plenty
plow
plump
porch
pose
praise
press
pretty
prince
probably
prop
proper
pry
puffy
putty

Q

R
racecourse
raft
railroad
rainy
rash
reporter
rinse
risky
roadwork
rotten
rut

Ruth

S
salty
Sam
scary
scroll
shade
shady
shark
she'd
shelf
she's
shootout
shortcake
shorts
shoulder
shove
sidewalk
sift
sled
sleepover
sleet
slept
slid
slouch
slump
snowball
snowy
splurge
starch
stash
stem
Steve
Steven
stew
stir
stitch
stony
stool
stray
streak
stress
stressful
stretch
stretchy
stuffing
stuffy

stunt
subject
suitcase
suppose

T
tasty
Ted
tense
they're
toolbox
toothpaste
trainer
tricky

U
underground
undershirt
understand

V
vane
vine
visit

W
waiter
wander
washing
website
wedding
weight
we'll
window
wise
wisely
woods
workshop

X

Y
YMCA
yoga
you'll
you've

Z

dr	tr	thr	sc	sk	sw
drape	trace	thread	scale	skater	swam
drawn	trance	threat	scald	sketch	Swede
dreamer	trend	threaten	scold	ski	Sweden
drench	tribe	thrift	scoop	skid	sweep
drift	troop	thrifty	scorch	skillful	sweeper
drill	trooper	thrill	scour	skinny	swept
drip	trout	throughout	Scotch	skip	swing
drug	truce		Scott	skull	Swiss

Words for Study

hardware	concerned	homey	savings
wrench	family	given	clothing
counter	etc.	dresser	although

Who Is Ginger?

Ginger was the lead singer with a band that played in many well-known clubs throughout the city. She had met Jerome about six months ago in a hardware store. She was buying a monkey wrench to fix a leaky pipe in her bathroom, and he was the clerk behind the counter. As far as Ginger was concerned, it was love at first sight. As for Jerome—well, who knew what went on in his mind?

Ginger lived on the third floor of a three-family house. She paid four hundred dollars a month for her rent and owned hardly anything in the way of couches, chairs, tables, etc. In fact, one of her four rooms had nothing in it at all.

Whenever her mother dropped by to see how Ginger was doing, she would scold her. "Goodness, Ginger, why don't you at least buy some rugs and paint the walls so this place would look a little more homey?"

But Ginger would just answer, "Well, you know that I don't make enough money with the band to do anything but pay the rent and buy food. Anyway, it's less work keeping a place clean when you don't own anything."

However, Ginger was not being truthful. She made a lot of money singing with the band and writing songs. She also made a lot of money giving voice lessons to children who wanted to be singers.

When Ginger was five years old, her grandmother had given her a piggy bank for her birthday. She had also given Ginger a card on which she had printed: "A penny saved is a penny earned."

Ginger had never forgotten this lesson on thrift. In fact, she still had the piggy bank on the floor in her bedroom. The reason it was on the floor was that Ginger didn't own a dresser.

The piggy bank was only used for small change now. For at twenty-five, which was Ginger's age, she had twenty-seven thousand dollars in a savings bank. She also owned quite a lot of land on the east side of town and had just bought a clothing store in a shopping center. And although Jerome didn't know it, she even owned the hardware store in which he worked.

1 About the Story. Answer these questions.

1. How did the name of the story help you understand what you read?

    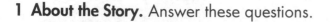 Who is Ginger   Ginger saving in having
    her own business

2. How did Ginger Mansfield earn her living?

    By singing in a band and writing songs and she owned a few
    business

3. For how long had Ginger known Jerome, and where did she meet him?

    Ginger known Jerome for six months and she meet him in
    a hardware store

4. What did Jerome Martin do to earn a living?

5. How did Ginger feel about Jerome?

    love at first sight

6. How did Jerome feel about Ginger?

    lots for Jerome don't know what was going on in his
    mind

7. What did Ginger's mother think about the place where Ginger lived?

    Her mother didn't like how her house look

8. How was Ginger not being truthful with her mother?

    lied about the money

What do you think?

9. How do you think Jerome would feel about Ginger if he knew how much money she had?

_____

_____

2 The Ending -ly. Add -ly to the words below. Then use these words in the sentences. Study the example before you begin.

✓late __lately__	mad __madly__
truthful __truthfully__	peaceful __peacefully__
proper __propely__	wild __wildly__
odd __oddly__	cost __costly__
shy __shyly__	live __lively__

1. Because John wasn't dressed __propely__, the mother of the groom would not allow him to enter the church for the wedding.

2. After the wedding, a little girl __shyly__ asked the bride if she could have her flowers.

3. Ginger did not speak __truthfully__ to her mother when she said she was broke.

4. Ginger was __madly__ in love with Jerome although she really didn't know why.

5. The boxer swung so __wildly__ in the fourth round that he lost his footing and fell into the ropes.

6. Getting his jeep fixed would have been so __costly__ that Dave decided it was time to buy a new one.

7. Ted's boss hadn't been feeling well **lately**, so he went to see the doctor.

8. The fiddler played such __lively__ tunes that all the dancers were worn out after the first hour.

9. Miguel was sleeping so __peacefully__ on the couch that Joan decided not to wake him up.

10. __Oddly__ enough, there were more men at the Mother's Day party than there were women.

3 Words That Mean the Same. Match each word below with the word that means nearly the same thing.

beginning	dense	gaze	pledge
bright	edgy	healthy	shove
brink	frighten	plead	stir

pledge   **1.** beg

brink   **2.** edge

edgy   **3.** jumpy

stir   **4.** mix

shove   **5.** push

frighten   **6.** scare

bright   **7.** shiny

gaze   **8.** stare

beginning   **9.** start

dense   **10.** thick

plead   **11.** vow

healthy   **12.** well

4 Compound Words. Find the two little words in each compound word, and put them on the lines to the right.

1. toothbrush   _tooth_ + _brush_

2. Thanksgiving   _Thanks_ + _giving_

3. overboard   _over_ + _board_

4. gumdrop   _gum_ + _drop_

5. flowerpot   _flower_ + _pot_

6. background   _back_ + _ground_

7. snowball   _snow_ + _ball_

8. seaweed   _sea_ + _weed_

9. highway   _high_ + _way_

10. crosswalk   _cross_ + _walk_

Review of Consonant Blends and Digraphs: Part 5

sm	sn	sp	scr	th	wh
smack	snatch	span	scram	theft	whack
smear	snarl	spark	scraper	thief	wham
Smith	sneak	speck	scratchy	thinner	wheeze
smog	sneakers	sped	screw	thirst	whether
smoky	sneaky	speech	script	thirsty	whichever
smooth	sniff	spit	scrounge	thorn	whatsoever
smoothly	snowstorm	spine	scruff	thud	whim
smudge		spaghetti		thump	whine

Words for Study

enjoy	loose	fingers	oozing
apartment	tilted	Tony	rags
fate	soles	exclaimed	buckets

A Strange Twist of Fate

Jerome was not a thief, but he did enjoy having sneaky ideas now and then. Right now he was thinking how nice it would be to snatch a can of blue paint from the top shelf to give to Ginger. He didn't have the money just now, but maybe he could pay for the paint out of next week's paycheck.

Jerome had not heard from Ginger for three weeks, and he missed her badly. Maybe this gift of paint would make her come to her senses. It also might be a way to trick Ginger into painting her apartment. "The nerve of her," thought Jerome, "calling my apartment a pigpen! At least I have rugs and books and pictures and armchairs for my friends to sit on when they drop by for a visit."

It was a slow night at the hardware store. "I'll just check to see if this is the right shade of blue," thought Jerome. "No harm in checking." Jerome reached for the five-gallon can of blue paint on the shelf.

What happened next is hard to describe. Through some strange twist of fate, the lid on the can was loose. When Jerome tilted the can toward him as he brought it down from the shelf, five gallons of blue paint poured all over him, the counter, and the floor. Jerome was covered with paint from the top of his head to the soles of his feet. He tried to get the bills and other papers on the counter out of the way, but all he did was smudge them badly with his blue fingers. Now nobody would ever be able to read them.

Just then his friend Tony walked in. "Wow, Jerome!" exclaimed Tony. "I knew you were feeling blue about what happened with Ginger, but I had no idea you were feeling this blue." Tony was laughing so hard that he nearly slipped on the paint that was oozing toward the door.

Jerome thought that if he opened his mouth it would fill with paint, so he just snarled at Tony. He pointed wildly at the bathroom where all the rags, mops, and buckets were kept. Seven hours later Jerome and Tony had wiped up the last of the mess. Jerome didn't know how he would explain the missing bills and papers to his boss. Right now he didn't care. All he wanted to do was crawl into his bed and sleep for three solid days.

1 About the Story. Answer these questions.

1. Where does this story take place? _____

2. What time of day does this story take place? _____

3. For what two reasons did Jerome think about giving Ginger some blue paint?

   a. _____

   b. _____

4. Describe what happened when Jerome went to check the can of paint.

   _____

   _____

5. How did Tony react when he saw what had happened to Jerome?

   _____

6. How long did it take Jerome and Tony to clean up the mess from the spilled paint?

   _____

What do you think?

7. Do you think Jerome was really going to take the paint?

   _____

8. If you were Jerome's boss, what would you say to Jerome when you learned that all the bills and papers on the counter were gone? _____

   _____

2 More Work with the Ending -ly. Add -ly to the words below. Then use these words in the sentences. Study the example before you begin.

✓fresh __freshly_____   hour _____

neat _____   tight _____

thick _____   rare _____

square _____   successful _____

common _____   certain _____

1. Sue folded her sweaters and placed them _____ in the dresser.

2. Since the birth of their baby, the Smiths _____ have a chance to go to the movies anymore.

3. The workers stated that if they didn't get a higher _____ wage, they would go out on strike next Monday.

4. The workers were _____ in a good mood when they were told that they would get the raise.

5. The smell of __freshly_____ baked cupcakes brought the whole family in from the back porch.

6. Miguel looked _____ into his wife's eyes and said, "This time, you're wrong."

7. Spaghetti is _____ served with tomato sauce.

8. Ms. Bond had curled her hair so _____ that she tossed and turned in her sleep all night.

9. Jim spread the jam so _____ on the toast that he could hardly eat it without making a mess.

10. John was able to get up _____ on the water skis on his third try.

3 Word Opposites. Match the words below with their opposites.

clear	frozen	loose	skinny
costly	given	rarely	tense
fake	hairy	risky	ugly

_____ **1.** bald

_____ **2.** cheap

_____ **3.** melted

_____ **4.** often

_____ **5.** plump

_____ **6.** pretty

_____ **7.** real

_____ **8.** relaxed

_____ **9.** safe

_____ **10.** smoky

_____ **11.** taken

_____ **12.** tight

4 Compound Words. Write the two little words that make up each compound word on the lines to the right.

1. dishrag _____ + _____

2. fingernail _____ + _____

3. tailspin _____ + _____

4. anymore _____ + _____

5. overdone _____ + _____

6. drugstore _____ + _____

7. fingerprint _____ + _____

8. bathtub _____ + _____

Review of Silent Letters

kn	wr	gn	tch	dge	gh *and* ght
knack	wrapper	gnash	notch	ledge	lighten
knapsack	wrapping	gnarled	Butch	lodge	lighter
knelt	wrecker	gnat	clutch	judge	tighten
knight	wren	gnaw	pitch	nudge	tightly
knob	wring	gnawing	pitcher	trudge	mighty
knee-deep	wrung	gnome	watchman	ridge	slight

Words for Study

involved	force	habits	unhealthy
afterward	nasty	brownies	dentist
Holly	nearby	restless	practice

At Yoga Class

Steven had a slight cold, but he decided to go to his yoga class anyway. He glanced at his watch and saw that he would have to leave right away if he was going to get there by eight o'clock.

Once he was in class, Steven became so involved in the new exercises they were learning that he forgot all about his cold. He was getting the knack of these exercises more quickly than he ever had before. Who knew? Maybe some day he would become a yoga teacher.

Afterward Holly, who worked out on the mat next to Steven, asked him if he wanted to go out for a cup of coffee. "Sure" said Steven between sneezes, "why not?" It seemed that the minute class ended, his cold came back in full force.

"That's a nasty cold you've got, Steve. Are you doing anything to get rid of it?" asked Holly as they sat down at the counter in a nearby coffee shop.

"No, I'll be all right" answered Steven.

"You know, I should lend you this book I have about yoga," said Holly. "It tells how yoga isn't just a matter of doing exercises. You also have to eat right and breathe right and change your bad habits. Yoga is a whole way of life. The book says that if you do these certain things, you never get sick or feel as if you're under a lot of stress."

"What does the book say about double-chocolate brownies?" laughed Steven, who had decided to order one.

"Chocolate brownies are awful for you!" exclaimed Holly.

"Oh, come on, Holly. One little brownie?" asked Steven.

"It's the sugar," Holly explained. "The book says sugar is one of the worst things in the world for

Lesson 7   **37**

you. It's a main cause of feeling grouchy and restless. It's also one of the main reasons why so many people are fat and unhealthy."

"You sound just like my dentist," laughed Steven, "and he doesn't even practice yoga." Then Steven sighed and said, "Well, so much for double-chocolate brownies." He was beginning to see that getting involved with yoga was like so many other things in life: there was more to think about than he thought there would be.

1 About the Story. Answer these questions.

1. How did Steven feel just before he left for his yoga class?

   _____

2. Why did Steven think that some day he might become a yoga teacher?

   _____

3. What did Holly ask Steven when the yoga class was over?

   _____

4. What did Holly think was so awful about brownies?

   _____

5. Does Steven order a double-chocolate brownie? How do you know?

   _____

   _____

6. What did Steven learn about yoga from talking to Holly?

   _____

   _____

7. This story takes place in three places. Name them in order.

   a. _____

   b. _____

   c. _____

2 The Endings -*ful* and -*less*.

A. Study the example and then add -*ful* or -*less* to the words.

rest + less = <u>restless</u>   stress + ful = _____

sugar + less = _____   spot + less = _____

arm + ful = _____   peace + ful = _____

harm + ful = _____   taste + less = _____

B. Study the example, and then match each word you wrote with the sentence that best describes it.

_____ **1.** This word describes how your life feels if your nerves are strained.

_____ **2.** This word describes how unsalted food might taste.

_____ **3.** This word describes what a dentist would say that sugar is.

_____ **4.** This word describes a huge load that a person is carrying.

_____ **5.** This word describes a person who feels very calm inside.

<u>restless</u> _____ **6.** This word describes a person who has trouble relaxing.

_____ **7.** This word describes a room that is really clean.

_____ **8.** This word describes the kind of chewing gum that Holly would chew.

3 Same or Opposite? If the pair of words means nearly the same thing, write *same* on the line to the right. If the pair of words doesn't mean the same thing at all, write *opposite* on the line.

1. ceiling   floor   _____

2. gloom   joy   _____

3. idea   thought   _____

4. knapsack   backpack   _____

5. nearby   close   _____

6. penny   cent   _____

7. strange   odd   _____

8. raise   lower   _____

9. scour   scrub   _____

10. smear   smudge   _____

11. stood   knelt   _____

12. vowels   *a, e, i, o, u*   _____

4 Compound Words. Find the two little words in each compound word, and put them on the lines to the right.

1. knockout   _____ + _____

2. shipwreck   _____ + _____

3. lifeguard   _____ + _____

4. matchbook   _____ + _____

5. lighthouse   _____ + _____

6. doorknob   _____ + _____

7. starfish   _____ + _____

8. comeback   _____ + _____

9. eyesight   _____ + _____

10. kneecap   _____ + _____

Review of Vowel Combinations: Part 1

ai	ee	ēa	ĕa	ui
aim	breeze	bead	dread	fruit
bait	geese	leap	dreadful	grapefruit
braid	greet	flea	tread	bruise
faith	greedy	plea	weather	cruise
Gail	Lee	pleased	feather	cruiser
hail	tee	veal	leather	juice
mailbox	teepee	grease	pleasant	juicy
waist		season		suit

Words for Study

softly	mailman	moments	bragging
folks	route	yeah	who's
agreed	expect	happiness	daily

Ginger Gives Some Advice

Gail slouched against the doorway of Ginger's apartment with a leather suitcase in her hand. There were bruises on her face, and she was crying softly.

"Gail!" cried Ginger. "What on earth happened? You look awful!"

"I don't want to put you to any trouble," sighed Gail as she put her suitcase down, "but is it okay if I stay here for a day or two? I hate to be by myself when I'm feeling like this."

"Sure" answered Ginger, "of course, it's all right. You want some grapefruit? I was just making breakfast. Tell me what happened."

"Skip the food. I'll just have some coffee. I'm too upset to eat anything," cried Gail.

"Gail, will you just sit down and tell me what happened?" pleaded Ginger.

"Well," Gail began, "I dropped by to see my folks. I wanted to ask them if they could lend me the money for a down payment on a new car. My father lost his temper and started complaining that the only time I ever visited them was when I needed some money. I started yelling, and the next thing I knew, my father told me not to come back until I learned to care more about human happiness than greed."

"So, how did you get those bruises?" asked Ginger. "Your father didn't hit you, did he?"

Gail shook her head. "No. I was so angry that, when I left, I banged my head against the front door. I don't think he even cared whether or not I was hurt. Oh, Ginger, it was just dreadful!"

"It sounds dreadful," agreed Ginger. "You know you do only go over there when you want money, and you should know by now how your father gets whenever the question of money comes up. When are you going to learn?"

Gail was really crying now. "He thinks he's such a big shot. Always bragging about how strong he is. A flea could knock him over. All he is is an old mailman who walks the same route day after day, year after year."

"What on earth has his job got to do with anything?" asked Ginger. "You know very well your father's proud of his job, and the fact that you're always putting him down for it doesn't help matters any. What do you expect him to do—kiss and hug you for calling him a dumb mailman who couldn't hurt a flea?"

Gail stared at Ginger for a few moments and then said slowly, "You know, Ginger, I never thought of it that way."

Ginger just said, "Yeah, well there are a lot of things you better start thinking about. Now go wash your face, and I'll fix you some breakfast."

1 About the Story. Answer these questions.

1. Where does this story take place? At Ginger apartment

2. What time of day do you think the story takes place? Why did you choose this time?
In the morning because of breakfast

3. What did Gail want from Ginger?
She want to stay with Ginger for a day or two

4. Why was Gail's father so angry with her?
Because she only comes around when she need money

5. Why was Gail's face so bruised?
Becaus she banged my head against the front door.

6. What advice did Ginger give Gail?
To stop pputs him down all the time

7. Does Gail live with her parents? How do you know?
No. Because she only go visit she need thingsome

What do you think?

8. Do you agree with Ginger's advice? (Be sure to explain your answer.)
Yes Because she should be respectful

2 More Work with the Endings -*ful* and -*less*.

A. Study the example and then add -*ful* or -*less* to the words.

count + less = _countless_

watch + ful = _watchful_

pain + less = _painless_

spoon + ful = _spoonful_

pain + ful = _painful_

faith + ful = _Faithful_

joy + ful = _joyful_

worth + less = _worthless_

home + less = _homeless_

sun + less = _sunless_

B. Study the example, and then match each word you wrote with the sentence that best describes it.

Homeless
Spoonful
Sunless

1. This word describes a family that doesn't have a place to live.

2. This is as much as a spoon will hold.

3. This word describes a gloomy day when there is hardly any sunlight.

Faithful
Painful
Watchful

4. This is another word to describe a person who is loyal.

5. This word describes something that hurts you very much.

6. This word describes a person who doesn't miss a trick because his eyes are always open.

Joyful

7. This word describes a feeling of great happiness.

countless

8. This word describes something that happens so many times that it's hard to keep track of the number.

Painless
Worthless

9. This word describes something that doesn't hurt you at all.

10. This word describes something that would bring a person very little money if he tried to sell it.

3 Same or Opposite? If the pair of words means nearly the same thing, write *same* on the line to the right. If the pair of words doesn't mean the same thing at all, write *opposite* on the line.

1. afterward   before   <u>Opposite</u>

2. aim   goal   <u>Same</u>

3. cluttered   messy   <u>Same</u>

4. dreadful   awful   <u>Same</u>

5. joyful   gloomy   <u>Opposite</u>

6. lively   dull   <u>Opposite</u>

7. mighty   strong   <u>Same</u>

8. nasty   kind   <u>Opposite</u>

9. nudge   poke   <u>Same</u>

10. pitcher   catcher   <u>Opposite</u>

11. pleased   troubled   <u>Opposite</u>

12. snarl   growl   <u>Same</u>

4 Compound Words. To find the answers, choose a word from **List A** and add a word from **List B** to it. Study the example before you begin.

List A	List B
cheap	baby
✓coffee	balls
cry	board
kin	✓cake
leap	cloth
meat	folks
news	fork
pitch	frog
score	line
spend	skate
waist	stand
wash	thrift

coffeecake

1. This is a kind of cake that is often served for breakfast.

newsstand

2. Many people stop here to buy the daily paper.

wash cloth

3. You use this when you take a shower.

meat balls

4. Many people like to eat these with spaghetti.

score board

5. The fans glance at this to see who's winning the game.

waist line

6. Many doctors think that you are unhealthy if this is too large.

leapfrog

7. In this game, a child jumps over the back of the child in front of him.

pitchfork

8. Farmers and others use this tool for tossing hay and straw.

crybaby

9. This person whines and complains when he doesn't get his own way.

Kinfolks

10. These people are related to you by birth.

cheapskate

11. This person refuses to spend money unless he really has to.

spendthrift

12. This person has a lot of trouble saving money. He wants to spend it all!

Word Index: Lessons 1–8

A
actor
advice
afford
afterward
agree
aim
already
although
anymore
apartment
ape
appear
armful
aside

B
backfire
background
backpack
bait
balance
bathing
bathtub
bead
beast
bedding
beg
beginning
bench
besides
bin
blackboard
blade
blank
blast
blend
blessing
blindly
blond
bloody
bloom
bother
brace
bracelet
brag
braid

brainy
branch
breast
breeze
bribe
broil
brownie
bruise
brush
bucket
building
Butch
buzz

C
camper
carpenter
certainly
chalk
chalkboard
cheapskate
cheat
chilly
chin
chore
chose
chow
chunk
clam
clammy
clash
clearing
clench
clerk
cling
clingy
clothing
clumsy
clung
clutch
clutter
coffeecake
comeback
coming
commonly
complain
concern

confuse
confusing
control
costly
counter
countless
cove
cramp
crate
crick
crosswalk
crow
crude
cruise
cruiser
crutch
crybaby
cuff
cutting

D
daily
dense
dentist
difference
dishpan
dishrag
dishwasher
doggy
dome
doorknob
dose
drape
drawn
dread
dreadful
dreamer
dreamland
drench
dresser
dressing
drift
drill
drip
drug
drugstore

E
earring
edge
edgy
enjoy
enter
etc.
eve
exclaim
exercise
expect
eyesight
eyestrain

F
faith
faithful
fallen
family
fate
feast
feather
figure
finger
fingernail
fingerprint
firelight
fisherman
fitting
flail
flap
flashlight
flea
flight
flighty
flirt
flowerpot
flute
folk(s)
footing
force
forgotten
freeway
freshly
fright
frighten
frog

frown
frozen

G
Gail
gale
gaze
geese
given
glance
globe
gloom
gloomy
glove
glumly
gnarled
gnash
gnat
gnaw
gnawing
gnome
gosh
grace
grandfather
grandmother
grapevine
grease
greedy
greet
grief
grouchy
growl
grudge
grumpy
gumdrop

H
habit
hail
hairbrush
hairy
handshake
happiness
hardware
headache
hem
highway

Holly
homemade
homey
hourly
how's
hush

I
icing
improve
involve
iron
ivy

J
Jerome
jet
joyful
judge
juice
juicy
jumpy

K
kin
kinfolk(s)
kitchen
knack
knapsack
knee-deep
knelt
knight
knob
knockout
knotting
knotty

L
lampshade
lately
lawyer
leaky
leap
leapfrog
leash
leather
ledge

Lee
lesson
lifeguard
lighten
lighter
lighthouse
lining
lively
lodge
loose
lower
Luke

M
madly
mailbox
mailman
mankind
Mansfield
Martin
mash
matchbook
mighty
Miguel
milkshake
mist
moment
mope
muscle

N
nasty
nearby
neatly
newspaper
newsstand
notch
nudge

O
oddly
ooze
overboard
overdone
overgrown
owe
ox

P

pact
padding
painful
painless
parent
paste
patty
pave
paving
peacefully
perch
pigpen
pinch
pitch
pitcher
pitchfork
plainly
plea
plead
pleasant
pleased
pledge
plenty
plow
plump
porch
pose
practice
praise
press
pretty
prince
probably
prop
proper
properly
pry
puffy
putty

Q

R

racecourse
raft
rag
railroad
rainy
rarely
rash
reporter
restless
ridge
rinse
risky
roadwork
rotten
route
rut
Ruth

S

salty
Sam
savings
scald
scale
scary
scold
scoop
scorch
scoreboard
Scotch
Scott
scour
scram
scraper
scratchy
screw
script
scroll

scrounge
scruff
season
seaweed
shade
shady
shark
she'd
shelf
she's
shipwreck
shootout
shopping
shortcake
shorts
shoulder
shove
shy
shyly
sidewalk
sift
skater
sketch
ski
skid
skillful
skinny
skip
skull
sled
sleepover
sleet
slept
slid
slight
slouch
slump
smack
smear
Smith
smog
smoky

smooth
smoothly
smudge
snarl
snatch
sneak
sneakers
sneaky
sniff
snowball
snowstorm
snowy
softly
sole
spaghetti
span
spark
speck
sped
speech
spendthrift
spine
spit
splurge
spoonful
square
squarely
starch
starfish
stash
stem
Steve
Steven
stew
stir
stitch
stony
stool
stray
streak
stress
stressful

stretch
stretchy
stuffing
stuffy
stunt
subject
successfully
suit
suitcase
sunless
suppose
swam
Swede
Sweden
sweep
sweeper
swept
Swiss

T

tailspin
tasteless
tasty
Ted
tee
teepee
tense
Thanksgiving
theft
they're
thickly
thief
thinner
thirst
thirsty
thorn
thread
threaten
thrift
thrifty
thrill
throughout

thud
thump
tighten
tightly
tilt
Tony
toolbox
toothbrush
toothpaste
trace
trainer
trance
tread
trend
tribe
tricky
troop
trooper
trout
truce
trudge
truthfully

U

underground
undershirt
understand
unhealthy

V

vane
veal
vine
visit
vow

W

waist
waistline
waiter
wander
washcloth

washing
watchman
weather
website
wedding
weight
we'll
whack
wham
whatsoever
wheeze
whether
whichever
whim
whine
who's
wildly
window
wise
wisely
woods
workshop
wrapper
wrapping
wrecker
wren
wrench
wring
wrung

X

Y

yeah
YMCA
yoga
you'll
you've

Z

Review of Vowel Combinations: Part 2

oa	oo	oo	ou	oi	oy
boast	boom	brook	pout	moist	Joyce
moan	goof	nook	pounce	hoist	loyally
oak	goofy	understood	sound	toil	loyalty
oats	roof	bookworm	bound	boiler	royally
oatmeal	moose	bookcase	lousy	void	royalty
poach	stoop	bookshelf	aloud	avoid	ahoy
throat		goodies	trousers	rejoice	

e-card	message	delete	despite
voice mail	invited	noticed	promise
e-mail	anyone	bottom	perform

Jerome Gets an E-Card

Jerome hadn't heard from Ginger in four weeks. He checked his voice mail and e-mail daily, hoping she would leave him a message. But she never got in touch with him.

Jerome felt lousy. He missed Ginger a lot. He wanted to hear the sound of her voice and see her goofy grin. But he was too proud to tell her he was sorry.

None of his friends understood. They told him to stop moaning about who was right and who was wrong. They said he should tell Ginger he was sorry. But Jerome couldn't bring himself to do it. His mood got worse and worse. He began to avoid his good friends. He didn't feel like leaving his house.

Jerome tried to pass the time by cooking and reading books. Soon enough, he had read everything on his bookshelf. Jerome decided to order some new books online. He turned on his laptop, and the computer made a beeping noise. The sound meant he had a new e-mail message. Maybe the message was from Ginger! She was bound to get in touch sooner or later, he thought.

Jerome opened the e-mail. Someone named Holly had sent him an e-card. The card invited him to a party at Holly's house. Jerome didn't know anyone named Holly. The card must be a mistake, he thought.

He was about to delete the card when he noticed a note at the bottom from Steven. Now everything made sense! Steven knew Jerome was avoiding his messages. He must have sent the card knowing Jerome would open it. Jerome laughed despite his bad mood. "That Steven is always plotting," he said aloud. Then he read the note.

"Jerome," the note began, "please stop avoiding me! You can't stay in your house for weeks on end. Come

to this party at Holly's house tonight. Holly is a woman in my yoga class. She is writing a health food cookbook. She's baking up a batch of goodies that she wants people to taste. I promise you'll have a good time. You can pout about Ginger as much as you want. Just come goof around and enjoy a night with your good friend Steven! I'll pick you up at eight."

Jerome looked at his watch. He only had half an hour to get ready. He changed into nice trousers and laced up his boots. He felt better already. Steven was right: Jerome had been spending too much time by himself. Thank goodness he had such a kind, loyal friend to help him get out of his lousy mood.

1 About the Story. Answer these questions.

1. Why was Jerome checking his voice mail and e-mail?

   Hoping he would here from Ginger

2. What did Jerome's friends tell him he should do?

   That he should tell Ginger he was sorry

3. Why did he go online that night?

   He decided to order some new book.

4. Why did Jerome almost delete the e-card he got?

   Jerome didn't know anyone name holly.

5. How did Steven make sure that Jerome would come to Holly's party?

   Steven told Jerome he would pict him up for the party.

6. What did Jerome agree with Steven about by the end of the story?

   Steven was right Jerome was spend to munh time by hisself

7. What is the difference between how Jerome feels at the beginning of the story and how he feels at the end of the story?

   He felt lousy at the begining at home the the in he was out of his lousy muving

What do you think?

8. Why won't Jerome tell Ginger that he is sorry?

He was to proud to tell her he was sorry

9. Is Jerome the kind of person you would like to have as a friend? (Be sure to explain your answer.) _Yes. Why because he have a good herat_

2 The Ending _-en._ Use the words below to fill in the blanks.

broken	forgotten	loosen	moisten	taken	weaken
fallen	frozen	mistaken	sunken	threaten	written

1. The rain had _frozen_ into ice on the street, causing cars to slide and crash.

2. Jerome had _fallen_ when he tried to stand on his head.

3. After two hours of hard work, the divers were able to hoist the _sunken_ chest up to the boat.

4. Joyce had been so busy working on the plans for the new computer that she had _forgotten_ all about her aunt's birthday.

5. When he woke up the next morning, the boxer wondered if winning the fight was really worth a _broken_ jaw.

6. The cab driver had _taken_ a wrong turn, and now he was lost.

7. The doctor told Ann that getting too little exercise could _weaken_ her heart.

8. The letter had been _written_ on such thin paper that Louise ripped it badly when she unfolded it.

9. Every few years, Scott would _threaten_ to quit his job if he did not get a raise.

10. Dave decided to _loosen_ his tie so he could breathe better.

11. Because Ruth didn't _moisten_ the stamp enough, it came off the letter as soon as she put it in the mailbox.

12. "If you think I'm going to wash all these dishes while you sit there and watch television, you're sadly _mistaken_!" Mike shouted.

3 Which Word Does Not Fit? Choose the word in each line that does not fit with the rest, and write it on the line to the right.

1. brother	friend	mother	sister	grandfather	*Friend*
2. hail	ice	ice cubes	sleet	slush	*ice cubes*
3. raincoat	moist	wet	damp	dripping	*raincoat*
4. butter	flour	salt	sugar	brownies	*brownies*
5. bake	beef	boil	fry	roast	*beef*
6. roar	scream	shout	speak	yell	*speak*
7. e-mail	website	mailman	Internet	computer	*mailman*
8. anyone	everyone	everything	no one	someone	*everything*
9. goof	clown	joker	promise	fool	*promise*
10. act	task	play	perform	put on	*task*

The Sound for *au*

haul	cause	auto	sauce	pause	caught
Paul	because	automobile	saucer	gauze	taught
fault	caution	autumn	saucepan	haunt	daughter
faulty	cautious	August	faucet	haunted	slaughter
				laundry	laundromat

Words for Study

machines	completed	repeated	together
quarters	slot	forgive	neither
responded	straightened	forgiven	nor

Jerome Goes to the Laundromat

Jerome hauled his laundry out to his automobile and threw it in the trunk. It was a rainy autumn morning, and Jerome decided he might as well do his laundry now and get it over with.

The laundromat was always such a drag. First you had to search for a parking space. Then you had to get your clothes from the trunk of the car to the machines without dropping them all over the place. Then you had to hope the machines were working properly. The last concern, of course, was getting all the clothes back home without losing anything.

Today wasn't so bad though. The only other person there was Holly. She had just found a machine that worked after having lost six quarters and two dimes. Not only was Jerome glad to see her again, but also she could tell him which machines to avoid.

"Hey, Holly," Jerome said. "Remember me? I'm a friend of Steve's. He brought me to your party last Saturday."

"Of course, I remember you," responded Holly who had just completed writing "Out of Order" signs for two of the washing machines. "It's good to see you again. You were feeling bad about some girl that night, weren't you?"

"Yeah, her name's Ginger," answered Jerome. "I still haven't seen her."

Holly thought for a moment before she spoke. "Have you tried?"

"Nope," said Jerome as he paused to empty some soap into the machine and push in the slot. "How about that!" he exclaimed. "On the first try, I got a machine that works right!"

"I don't understand you at all," said Holly. "If you like this girl so much, why don't you try to see her and get things straightened out?"

"Because," Jerome explained, "it's her fault."

"Even so, you're the one who wants to see her."

"It's her fault," Jerome repeated. "She's the one who hung up on me, so she's the one who should call up and say how sorry she is for being such a jerk. Then maybe I would forgive her."

"If anybody is a jerk, Jerome, it's you," said Holly. "You're the one who needs to be forgiven."

"You women," laughed Jerome. "You stick together like glue. Well, just to show you there's no hard feelings, I'll buy you a Coke." He put quarters into the Coke machine, but neither Coke nor his quarters came out.

"Serves you right," laughed Holly.

1 About the Story. Answer these questions.

1. List three reasons that explain why Jerome thought going to the laundromat was a drag.

   a. _____

   b. _____

   c. _____

2. Describe what Holly was doing when Jerome came into the laundromat.

   _____

3. How many washing machines did Holly try before she found one that worked?

   _____

4. What two clues in the story told you how many washing machines Holly tried before she found one that worked?

   a. _____

   b. _____

5. Why hadn't Jerome called up Ginger yet?

   _____

6. Why did Holly think that Jerome should call up Ginger?

_____

7. Why did Holly tell Jerome that he was a jerk?

_____

What do you think?

8. Do you think Jerome should call up Ginger? Why or why not?

_____

_____

2 More Work with the Ending _-en._ Use the words below to fill in the blanks.

beaten	deepen	eaten	given	rotten	spoken
bitten	driven	fallen	ridden	shaken	straightened

1. Because a new driver had _____ the bus on Monday, it was twenty minutes late.

2. Becky decided to put off raking her yard until all the leaves had _____ from the trees.

3. Lee was so _____ when she fell off the horse that she vowed she would never ride again.

4. The dentist told Mr. Downs that it would cost over a thousand dollars to have his daughter's teeth _____.

5. What does it mean when somebody tells you that you have _____ off more than you can chew?

6. After the Brown children had _____ their Thanksgiving dinner, they were so full that they had no room for the pie.

7. Paul had not _____ to Joyce for so long that he had forgotten what her voice sounded like.

8. Even though the team was badly _____, the fans clapped loyally as the players came off the field.

9. Tim would have _____ his daughter a lift into town, but she wanted to walk with her friends.

10. Have you ever _____ a horse?

11. Jerome knew that if he kept seeing Ginger his feelings for her would _____.

12. When you have had a _____ day at work, do you look forward to better days, or do you feel that everything is hopeless?

3 Which Word Does Not Fit? Choose the word in each line that does not fit with the rest, and write it on the line to the right.

1. newspaper	reporter	teacher	teller	writer	_____
2. August	February	January	May	month	_____
3. ace	deck	jack	king	queen	_____
4. brick	building	iron	steel	wood	_____
5. ant	flea	gnat	bee	pest	_____
6. blues	drum	folk	jazz	hip-hop	_____
7. cup	glass	plate	saucer	saucepan	_____
8. auto	highway	jeep	truck	van	_____
9. chestnut	elm	ivy	oak	pine	_____
10. autumn	season	spring	summer	winter	_____
11. catfish	eel	perch	shark	whale	_____
12. England	France	Rome	Spain	Sweden	_____

4 Spelling Check. The answers to the clues are listed at the left. As you can see, the letters of the words are all mixed up. Spell the words the right way on the lines.

a a b e f k r s t

1. _____ This is the first meal of the day.

a a b e h l p t

2. _____ This begins with the letter *a* and ends with the letter *z*.

a a m m m l

3. _____ This animal feeds its young with milk.

a C h i m r s s t

4. _____ Some people celebrate this day by giving gifts which have been placed under a tree or in stockings.

c d o o r t

5. _____ Some people go to this person when they feel sick.

c e e f f o

6. _____ Some people like it black; others put cream and sugar in it.

e d d g i n w

7. _____ You will find a bride and groom here.

i m o r r r

8. _____ You look at yourself in this to make sure you look all right.

i S s s w

9. _____ This kind of cheese has holes in it.

e e h i n r t t

10. _____ Many people think this number brings bad luck.

ar	er	ir	or	ur
darn	concert	sir	cord	fur
harp	cancer	Kirk	cork	further
lard	perk	chirp	corpse	blurt
barge	Herb	birch	forbid	lurch
charge	herb	fir	forth	murder
barber	berserk	circus	forge	murmur
farther	weren't	circle	gorge	hurl
apart	nervous	squirm	stork	jury

Words for Study

bordered	daydreaming	spied
peanut	breed	single
sandwiches	listen	sideshow

The Camping Trip

Even if Jerome had decided to call Ginger, he wouldn't have been able to reach her. In the first place, Ginger had had her cell phone shut off. As she saw it, no phone would mean one less bill to pay. In the second place, Ginger had gone to camp out on a piece of land she owned up north. This was just what she needed, she reasoned, to perk her up after her trouble with Jerome. Men!

On the third day Ginger was camping, she hiked on a path that she hadn't been on before. The path was bordered by huge fir trees and pine trees. Birds chirped from the branches, and squirrels searched for food.

After Ginger had hiked about five miles, she sat down under a birch tree and gorged on peanut butter sandwiches and brownies. How peaceful it was! There was no way that anybody could barge in on her here. There were no newspapers filled with the latest murder stories and cancer scares and no shows or concerts to have to get ready for.

Ginger did not have to report back to the band until next Thursday. She was daydreaming about never having to work again when she thought she heard a growling sound from farther down the path.

"Oh, no!" cried Ginger. Her pleasant daydream quickly turned into an awful picture of being eaten by some strange breed of wild animal. "Why," thought Ginger out loud, "didn't I listen to my mother?" Ginger's mother was always harping on the fact that young women *never* go camping alone.

By now, Ginger was so nervous that she couldn't tell if she had really heard an animal or not.

However, this was certainly no time to go berserk. She calmly put the sandwiches and brownies in her backpack, slowly got up, and then ran for her life. The once-peaceful woods now seemed filled with strange and threatening sounds.

Ginger had run about half a mile when she spied two fishermen wading in a stream. She yelled with all her might to the men, who were so surprised that they nearly lost their footing and fell into the stream.

"When I get back to the city," screamed Ginger as she lurched toward the men, "I'm going to carry my cell phone everywhere, paint my whole apartment, and read every single newspaper I can find!"

Needless to say, the men thought she was nuts.

1 About the Story. Answer these questions.

1. Give two reasons why Jerome couldn't have gotten in touch with Ginger even if he had wanted to.

   a. _____

   b. _____

2. What was Ginger daydreaming about just before she thought she heard the growl of a strange animal?

   _____

3. List three things Ginger vowed to do as soon as she got back to the city.

   a. _____

   b. _____

   c. _____

4. Why does Ginger now look forward to her life in the city?

   _____

5. In one or two sentences, tell what happened in this story.

   _____

   _____

What do you think?

6. Do you think Ginger really heard a wild animal? Give a reason for your answer.

_____

7. Do you feel safer in the city or the woods?

_____

2 Words That Begin with _re-_. Use the words below to fill in the blanks. (Use the rules you have learned to sound out the new words.)

react	recover	rejected	remarks	require	reveal
recall	refuse	rejection	repeat	respect	

1. The main reason that Jerome didn't call Ginger was that he had no idea how she would

_____.

2. He didn't want to face the fact that Ginger might _____ to see him again.

3. Jerome made some rude _____ about Ginger.

4. However, the truth was that he had a lot of _____ for her.

5. His problem was that he didn't want to _____ his true feelings to Ginger because he thought he might get hurt.

6. Jerome could still _____ the first time a girl had told him she didn't want to see him anymore.

7. It had happened during his second year of high school, and it had taken him the rest of high school to _____ from it.

8. Jerome certainly didn't want to _____ this kind of pain with Ginger.

9. None of us likes to be _____, but Jerome was so scared of _____ that it kept him from calling someone he really loved.

10. Jerome would _____ a lot more than just one talk in the laundromat with Holly to change his mind.

3 Words That Mean the Same. Match the words below with the words that mean nearly the same thing.

boast	juicy	mistaken	recall	require
faithful	lousy	nervous	rejoice	respond

_____ **1.** awful   _____ **6.** loyal

_____ **2.** answer   _____ **7.** moist

_____ **3.** brag   _____ **8.** need

_____ **4.** celebrate   _____ **9.** remember

_____ **5.** edgy   _____ **10.** wrong

4 What Is Where? Put the words below under the proper heading.

bleach	exercise bikes	pool
coin machines	grill	waitress
dryers	oven	yoga class

A Laundromat	A YMCA	A Diner
1. _____	1. _____	1. _____
2. _____	2. _____	2. _____
3. _____	3. _____	3. _____

5 What Is Where? Put the words below under the proper heading.

center field	drums	scoreboard
clowns	flutes	sideshows
dancing bears	pitchers	stage

A Circus	A Concert	A Baseball Game
1. _____	1. _____	1. _____
2. _____	2. _____	2. _____
3. _____	3. _____	3. _____

Review of Vowels Followed by the Letter *l*

al	el	il	ol	ul
gall	elf	dill	colt	gulf
malt	elk	sill	volt	gull
palm	elbow	silk	mold	gully
waltz	jelly	pill	moldy	sulk
wallet	well-done	pillow	troll	sulky
Walter	hotel	filter	roller	bulk
	motel	wilt	holder	bulky
	shelter	William	control	adult

Words for Study

video	arrived	bowl	workout
system	special	golf	movement
excited	spaceships	tennis	ease

Steven's New Game

It was Saturday afternoon, and Steven had just returned home from the mall. He had bought a brand-new video game system. He invited Holly over to play some of the games. Holly wasn't thrilled about the idea, but she could tell that Steven was really excited.

When Holly arrived, Steven was full of energy. He couldn't wait to try out his new system.

"So what's so special about this video game system?" Holly asked. She thought video games were silly. They were meant for children, not for adults. She didn't want to spend all day shooting spaceships or killing trolls.

"This is a new kind of game system," Steven said. "You control the games by moving your body around! You can bowl, golf, and play tennis. It's so cool! You can get a workout while you play."

Big deal, Holly thought to herself. A video game is a video game. What a dull way to spend a day.

"We can start with a game of golf," Steven said.

Steven showed Holly how to hold the video control and swing her arms like she was playing golf. It took her some time to get used to the game, but she did get a few of the golf balls to go in the holes. Next, Steven started a baseball game. He held the control and swung his arms like he was swinging a baseball bat. Holly tried, but the movement made her elbow sore.

"Do you have any games that don't involve sports?" Holly asked. She was feeling a little grumpy because Steven kept winning. "I'm not a big fan of golf or baseball," she said. "Is there a game that's more like yoga?"

"Well, there is a dancing game," Steven said in a sulky voice. He wanted to keep playing baseball. He was not a good dancer.

"That sounds great!" Holly exclaimed. Steven couldn't refuse, since she'd been such a good sport.

The dancing game brought out Steven's clumsy side. He tripped and missed steps. Holly, on the other hand, performed every dance move with ease. She was a natural dancer. Steven couldn't keep up.

"Don't sulk, Steven, you'll get the hang of it," Holly said. But she couldn't help laughing when Steven tripped. After half an hour, Steven was ready to call it quits. Holly wanted to play more.

"I could play this game all day," she said. Steven rolled his eyes and flopped down on the couch. He hoped she didn't really plan to stay all day!

1 About the Story. Answer these questions.

1. What did Steven buy and where did he buy it?

_____

2. Why did Holly think video games were silly?

_____

3. Give two reasons why Steven's new video game system is special.

   a. _____

   b. _____

4. Describe how Steven moved the control to play the baseball game.

_____

5. Why did Holly want to switch to the dancing game?

_____

6. Describe Holly and Steven as dancers. _____

_____

What do you think?

7. Why do you think Holly wanted to keep playing the video game, but Steven wanted to stop?

_____

_____

2 More Work with Words That Begin with re-. Use the words below to fill in the blanks. (Use the rules you have learned to sound out the new words.)

record	reduce	refund	remove	report	retreat
recovered	refresh	related	repair	retired	return

1. The worker got a _____ for paying too much in taxes.

2. Dick was unable to _____ the grease stains from his shirt, so he decided to use it as a rag.

3. Grace knew her parents would be angry when they saw her _____ card.

4. Luke didn't get the grass cut last Saturday because it took him all afternoon to _____ the lawn mower.

5. When William wanted to _____ himself, he took a long shower.

6. Kirk had put on twenty-three pounds during the winter months, and he knew he would have to _____ if his spring clothes were going to fit him right.

7. The first thing Louise wanted to do when she _____ from her job was move to a warmer state.

8. Walter was surprised when his mother told him that all the people who had come to the wedding were _____ to him.

9. After Rose _____, the doctor told her that she still had to take it easy for a few months.

10. On her way to the movie, Ms. Hall stopped by the store to _____ the shirt that did not fit her.

11. After the battle, the army was ordered to _____ to a hill further away from the field.

12. Ruth tried to _____ the television show so she wouldn't miss it.

3 Compound Words. To find the answers, choose a word from **List A** and add a word from **List B** to it. Study the example before you begin.

List A	List B
court	back
day	basket
dead	break
egg	ground
✓foot	line
home	overs
left	✓print
luke	room
paper	shell
play	sick
stand	still
waste	warm

footprint   1. This word is a mark made by the foot.

_____ 2. This word describes a meal that you save for later.

_____ 3. This word is the hard covering of a bird's egg.

_____ 4. This word is the latest time by which something must be done.

_____ 5. This word describes how you feel if you long to be home.

_____ 6. This is another word for dawn.

_____ 7. This is another word for everything coming to a full stop.

_____ 8. This is for papers and other trash that you want to throw away.

_____ 9. This word describes a book with a soft cover.

_____ 10. This is where the jury sits to hear a case.

_____ 11. This word describes something that is neither hot nor cold.

_____ 12. You find children playing on swings here.

4 Word Opposites. Match the words below with the words that are opposite in meaning.

adult	bulky	moldy	repair	sulky
arrived	excited	natural	scratchy	wilt

_____ **1.** bloom   _____ **6.** fresh

_____ **2.** bored   _____ **7.** happy

_____ **3.** break   _____ **8.** left

_____ **4.** child   _____ **9.** silky

_____ **5.** fake   _____ **10.** thin

A

actor
adult
advice
afford
afterward
agree
ahoy
aim
aloud
already
although
anymore
anyone
apart
apartment
ape
appear
armful
arrive
aside
August
auto
automobile
autumn
avoid

B

backfire
background
backpack
bait
balance
barber
barge
bathing
bathtub
bead
beast
beaten
bedding
beg
beginning
bench
berserk
besides
bin
birch
bitten
blackboard
blade
blank
blast
blend
blessing
blindly
blond
bloody
bloom

blues
blurt
boast
boiler
bookcase
bookshelf
bookworm
boom
border
bother
bottom
bound
bowl
brace
bracelet
brag
braid
brainy
branch
breast
breed
breeze
bribe
broil
broken
brook
brownie
bruise
brush
bucket
building
bulk
bulky
Butch
buzz

C

camper
camping
carpenter
caution
cautious
certainly
chalk
chalkboard
cheapskate
cheat
chestnut
chilly
chin
chirp
chore
chose
chow
chunk
circle
circus
clam
clammy
clash

clearing
clench
clerk
cling
clingy
clothing
clumsy
clung
clutch
clutter
coffeecake
colt
comeback
coming
commonly
complain
complete
concern
concert
confuse
confusing
control
cord
cork
corpse
costly
counter
countless
courtroom
cove
covering
cramp
crate
crick
crosswalk
crow
crude
cruise
cruiser
crutch
crybaby
cuff
cutting

D

daily
darn
daughter
daybreak
daydream
deadline
deepen
delete
dense
dentist
despite
difference
dill
dishpan
dishrag

dishwasher
diver
doggy
dome
doorknob
dose
drape
drawn
dread
dreadful
dreamer
dreamland
drench
dresser
dressing
drift
drill
drip
driven
drug
drugstore
dryer

E

earring
ease
eaten
e-card
edge
edgy
elbow
elf
elk
e-mail
enjoy
enter
etc.
eve
excite
exclaim
exercise
expect
eyesight
eyestrain

F

faith
faithful
fallen
family
farther
fate
faucet
fault
faulty
feast
feather
figure
filter
finger

fingernail
fingerprint
fir
firelight
fisherman
fitting
flail
flap
flashlight
flea
flight
flighty
flirt
flowerpot
flute
folk(s)
footing
footprint
forbid
force
forge
forgive
forgiven
forgotten
forth
freeway
freshly
fright
frighten
frog
frown
frozen
fur
further

G

Gail
gale
gall
gauze
gaze
geese
given
glance
globe
gloom
gloomy
glove
glumly
gnarled
gnash
gnat
gnaw
gnawing
gnome
golf
goodies
goof
goofy
gorge

gosh
grace
grandfather
grandmother
grapevine
grease
greedy
greet
grief
grouchy
growl
grudge
grumpy
gulf
gull
gully
gumdrop

H

habit
hail
hairbrush
hairy
handshake
happiness
hardware
harp
haul
haunt
haunted
headache
health food
hem
Herb
herb
highway
hip-hop
hoist
holder
Holly
homemade
homesick
homey
hotel
hourly
how's
hurl
hush

I

icing
improve
invite
involve
iron
ivy

J

jelly
Jerome

jet
Joyce
joyful
judge
juice
juicy
jumpy
jury

K

kin
kinfolk(s)
Kirk
kitchen
knack
knapsack
knee-deep
knelt
knight
knob
knockout
knotting
knotty

L

lampshade
lard
lately
latest
laundromat
laundry
lawyer
leaky
leap
leapfrog
leash
leather
ledge
Lee
leftover
lesson
lifeguard
lighten
lighter
lighthouse
lining
listen
lively
lodge
loose
loosen
lousy
lower
loyally
loyalty
Luke
lukewarm
lurch

M

machine
madly
mailbox
mailman
malt
mankind
Mansfield
Martin
mash
matchbook
message
mighty
Miguel
milkshake
mist
mistaken
moan
moist
moisten
mold
moldy
moment
moose
mope
motel
movement
murder
murmur
muscle

N

nasty
nearby
neatly
neither
nervous
newspaper
newsstand
nook
nor
notch
notice
nudge

O

oak
oat
oatmeal
oddly
ooze
overboard
overdone
overgrown
owe
ox

P

pact
padding
painful
painless

paperback
parent
paste
patty
Paul
pause
pave
paving
peacefully
peanut
perch
perform
perk
pigpen
pillow
pinch
pitch
pitcher
pitchfork
plainly
player
playground
plea
plead
pleasant
pleased
pledge
plenty
plow
plump
poach
porch
pose
pounce
pout
practice
praise
press
pretty
prince
probably
promise
prop
proper
properly
pry
puffy
putty

Q

quarter

R

racecourse
raft
rag
railroad
rainy
rarely
rash
recall
recover

refresh
reject
rejection
rejoice
remark
repair
repeat
reporter
require
respect
respond
restless
retire
retreat
reveal
ridden
ridge
rinse
risky
roadwork
roller
Rome
roof
rotten
route
royally
royalty
rut
Ruth

S

salty
Sam
sandwich
saucepan
saucer
savings
scald
scale
scary
scold
scoop
scorch
scoreboard
Scotch
Scott
scour
scram
scraper
scratchy
screw
script
scroll
scrounge
scruff
season
seaweed
shade
shady
shaken
shark
she'd

shelf
shelter
she's
shipwreck
shootout
shopping
shortcake
shorts
shoulder
shove
shy
shyly
sideshow
sidewalk
sift
silk
silky
sill
single
sir
skater
sketch
ski
skid
skillful
skinny
skip
skull
slaughter
sled
sleepover
sleet
slept
slid
slide
slight
slot
slouch
slump
smack
smear
Smith
smog
smoky
smooth
smoothly
smudge
snarl
snatch
sneak
sneakers
sneaky
sniff
snowball
snowstorm
snowy
softly
sole
sooner
spaceship
spaghetti
span

spark
special
speck
sped
speech
spendthrift
spied
spine
spit
splurge
spoken
spoonful
square
squarely
squirm
standstill
starch
starfish
stash
steel
stem
Steve
Steven
stew
stir
stitch
stocking
stony
stool
stoop
stork
straighten
stray
streak
stress
stressful
stretch
stretchy
stuffing
stuffy
stunt
subject
successfully
suit
suitcase
sulk
sulky
sunken
sunless
suppose
swam
Swede
Sweden
sweep
sweeper
swept
Swiss
system

T

tailspin
tasteless

tasty
taught
Ted
tee
teepee
tennis
tense
Thanksgiving
theft
they're
thickly
thief
thinner
thirst
thirsty
thorn
thread
threaten
thrift
thrifty
thrill
throughout
thud
thump
tighten
tightly
tilt
together
toil
Tony
toolbox
toothbrush
toothpaste
trace
trainer
trance
tread
trend
tribe
tricky
troll
troop
trooper
trousers
trout
truce
trudge
truthfully

U

underground
undershirt
understand
understood
unhealthy

V

vane
veal
video
vine
visit

voice mail
void
volt
vow

W

waist
waistline
waiter
waitress
wallet
Walter
waltz
wander
warmer
washcloth
washing
wastebasket
watchman
weaken
weather
website
wedding
weight
we'll
well-done
weren't
whack
wham
whatsoever
wheeze
whether
whichever
whim
whine
who's
wildly
William
wilt
window
wise
wisely
woods
workout
workshop
wrapper
wrapping
wrecker
wren
wrench
wring
wrung

X

Y

yeah
YMCA
yoga
you'll
you've

Z

Review of the Hard and Soft *c* and *g*

The hard *c* as in *candy*, *cost*, and *cutting*:

cannot	carpet	cardboard	cocoa
coconut	corner	cob	cobweb
contain	Cuban	cockroach	cure

The soft *c* as in *cellar*, *city*, and *pounce*:

cider	cinder	Cinderella	cinch
Grace	force	lance	prance
mince	mincemeat	dunce	fancy

The hard *g* as in *gas*, *get*, *goof*, and *log*:

gain	gear	gob	gobble
gag	garlic	glee	forgive
forgiven	tag	gross	gust
gut	gutter		

The soft *g* as in *Ginger*, *George*, and *forge*:

gee	gem	gentle	cringe
gently	binge	gentleman	lunge
merge	verge	manager	grungy
plunge	urge		

Words for Study

quarrel	borrow	music	themselves
scheme	CD	salsa	except
convince	favorite	indulge	despair

Jerome's Scheme

Jerome decided he and Ginger needed to work out their quarrel face to face. He felt certain that once they saw each other, they wouldn't be able to stay angry. So Jerome came up with a scheme. He would throw a dance party Friday night and invite Ginger, who loved to dance. The only thing he couldn't figure out was how to get Ginger to come over to his place. It didn't help that she hated his messy apartment.

On Wednesday night, Tony called to tell Jerome that Ginger was back in town. Jerome told Tony about his plan and his problem.

"I'll convince her to come with me," Tony said. "It will be a cinch. She won't be able to turn down a party with good friends! Don't worry, you can count on me."

Jerome couldn't contain his glee. In just a few days, he would see Ginger and all would be forgiven! Jerome started cleaning his apartment right away. He bought two cans of bug spray to kill the cockroaches in the kitchen. He cleared the cobwebs from the ceiling. He scrubbed the carpet and was on the verge of washing the windows when he decided, "Enough is enough! I'll put a piece of cardboard where the glass is cracked, and that's it."

Jerome called Steven and asked to borrow the dancing game that Holly loved. She'd told him all about it at her party. It seemed like fun. Then he went online and burned a CD of Ginger's favorite hip-hop songs. He added some Cuban music, since Ginger liked salsa dancing.

Next, he went on a shopping binge. He bought cider, cocoa, cold cuts, garlic bread, cheese, crackers, and coconut cake. As much as Jerome had enjoyed Holly's party, the food had been gross. He wanted his guests to indulge and enjoy themselves.

On Friday, the party didn't get into gear until about ten o'clock. By one o'clock, the apartment was a wreck. The guests had gobbled up the food, the carpet was covered with crumbs and spilled cider, and paper cups and plates were tossed everywhere. Jerome's CD was a big hit. Everyone was dancing except Jerome. He sat by himself in a corner of the room.

Ginger and Tony hadn't stopped by. Jerome had called Tony's cell phone, but the calls went to voice mail. Where were those two? Had they confused the date of the party? Were they out on a date with each other? The thought made him cringe.

Jerome plunged into despair. He had the urge to kick everyone out of the party. He wanted to sit in his grungy apartment, alone, and sulk. Luckily for my guests, I'm too much of a gentleman to do so, he thought. He threw himself down on the couch and counted the hours, waiting for the party to end.

1 About the Story. Answer these questions.

1. Why had Jerome decided to have a party? _____
   _____

2. How was Tony involved in Jerome's scheme? _____
   _____

3. List three things that Jerome did to clean the apartment for the party.
   a. _____
   b. _____
   c. _____

4. What kind of music did Jerome burn on the CD for Ginger?
   _____

5. What thought made Jerome cringe? _____

6. What stopped Jerome from kicking everyone out of his apartment?
   _____

What do you think?

7. What do you think might have happened to Tony and Ginger? _____
   _____

2 Word Opposites. Match the words below with the words that are opposite in meaning.

borrow	despair	forgive	grungy	plunge
contain	except	gain	merge	quarrel

_____ **1.** clean

_____ **2.** also

_____ **3.** rise

_____ **4.** glee

_____ **5.** stay apart

_____ **6.** blame

_____ **7.** lose

_____ **8.** get along

_____ **9.** leave out

_____ **10.** lend

3 Which Word Fits Best? Choose the right word from the four choices and put it on the line.

1. Salsa is to dance as _____ is to music.

    a. horn   b. hip-hop   c. play   d. beat

2. Belt is to waist as glove is to _____.

    a. finger   b. wool   c. hand   d. palm

3. State is to California as city is to _____.

    a. Boston   b. country   c. sidewalks   d. streetlights

4. Grapefruit is to sour as _____ is to sweet.

    a. coffeecake   b. cracker   c. spaghetti   d. salty

5. Reveal is to show as convince is to _____.

    a. hidden   b. talk out of   c. talk into   d. love

6. Gill is to fish as _____ is to human.

    a. air   b. breath   c. breathe   d. lung

7. Wade is to water as hike is to _____.

    a. boots   b. land   c. march   d. trudge

8. Ice is to solid as _____ is to gas.

    a. liquid   b. steam   c. stove   d. water

9. Overdone is to raw as _____ is to fresh.

    a. new   b. ripe   c. rude   d. stale

10. Then is to now as past is to _____.

    a. last year   b. next year   c. present   d. tomorrow

11. Murmur is to soft as _____ is to loud.

    a. wheeze   b. speak   c. roar   d. say

12. Sunday is to week as January is to _____.

    a. month   b. thirty-one days   c. time   d. year

4 Consonants. A *consonant* is any letter of the alphabet that is not a vowel. Each of the words listed below has a double consonant. To help you sound out the word, draw a line between the double consonant and mark the *first* vowel short. Then say the word out loud. Study the example before you begin.

1. gutter   _gŭt - ter_   7. mammal _____

2. matter _____   8. rotten _____

3. summer _____   9. pepper _____

4. happen _____   10. slipper _____

5. cannot _____   11. quarrel _____

6. cutting _____   12. gobble _____

fight	eight	caught	bought
sight	eighty	taught	brought
height	freight	daughter	fought
fright	weight	slaughter	sought
frighten		naughty	ought
bright			
overnight			

sigh	weigh	laugh	tough	cough	dough
high	sleigh	laughter	rough		doughnut
	neighbor		enough		
	neighborhood				

Words for Study

shown	spying	driveway	arrested
station	pranks	insisted	harassing
Darkpill	doorbell	property	sons

Whatever Happened to Tony and Ginger?

The reason Tony and Ginger hadn't shown up for Jerome's party was that they had spent most of the night at the police station. This is what happened.

A year ago, Tony had bought a small house on the north side of town. For the first eight months, he and his neighbor, Mrs. Darkpill, had been on very good terms. This was odd because everybody else in the neighborhood avoided Mrs. Darkpill and her family.

Mrs. Darkpill spent most of her time spying on the neighbors. She kept out of sight, hidden behind her curtains, but she was always watching. If a neighbor parked his car on the street overnight or raked leaves into the gutter, Mrs. Darkpill was the first person to report him.

The Darkpill children were very naughty. The daughters fought with each other from noon to night. They liked to play pranks on the neighbors. They would ring the doorbell and run away or knock over a full trash can in the driveway. If anyone caught them, the girls would break down into fits of laughter.

Although other neighbors had gone through rough times with the Darkpills, Tony hadn't run into any problems. Then, four months ago, Mrs. Darkpill began to complain to Tony about the chestnut tree in his backyard. She thought the tree had grown too high. She claimed it blocked out all the bright sunlight that used to reach her house. The tree, she insisted, was really on her property, and she wanted it cut down at once.

Tony checked his deed to the property, and it was clear that Mrs. Darkpill was wrong. Tony brought the deed over to show her, but she didn't even look at it.

That's when the trouble began. Every morning at five o'clock for three weeks straight, Tony woke up to the sound of a buzz saw. It seemed that Mrs. Darkpill planned to remove the branches of his lovely chestnut tree one by one. Tony tried to talk some sense into her, but it didn't work.

One day, Tony caught the Darkpill kids letting the air out of his car tires. He started yelling at the girls, and Mrs. Darkpill called the police. She told the cops that Tony ought to be arrested for harassing her children. After that, Tony avoided the Darkpills. He was frightened they would press false charges against him.

Now what does all this have to do with the fact that Tony and Ginger missed Jerome's party? The answer to that question is in the next story.

1 About the Story. Answer these questions.

1. Describe how Mrs. Darkpill spends most of her time.

_____

_____

2. What were Mrs. Darkpill's reasons for wanting the chestnut tree cut down?

_____

_____

3. What did Mrs. Darkpill tell the police about Tony?

_____

_____

4. Why did Tony start to avoid Mrs. Darkpill and her family?

_____

_____

What do you think?

5. What would you do if a person like Mrs. Darkpill were your neighbor?

_____

_____

2 The *gh* and *ght* Words. Use the words below to fill in each blank.

bright	eight	neighbor	rough
cough	enough	ought	sighed
daughters	height	right	sleigh
dough	might	right	tough

1. Although I do try with all my _____,

   I can't seem to get those *g-h-t* words _____.

2. When I see *g-h-t* words, I choke and cough.

   Their crazy spellings just turn me _____ off.

3. I asked my _____ if he could tell why

   these rules were made, but he only _____.

4. "It's strange," he laughed sadly." They _____ to know better

   than to teach sons and _____ these nasty old letters."

5. Now bread's made from _____ which is smooth and not _____.

   A _____ means you're sick. Strong arms mean you're _____.

6. You ride in a _____. To play basketball, you need _____.

   After seven comes _____. When the sun's out, it's _____.

7. Well, I have no idea how I'll learn all this stuff.

   I'm going out with my friends now, 'cause I've had _____!

3 Same or Opposite? If the words in each pair mean the same thing, write *same* on the line to the right. If they do not mean the same thing, write *opposite* on the line.

1. a lot   plenty   _____

2. blank   empty   _____

3. brook   stream   _____

4. clearing   woods   _____

5. dunce   know-it-all   _____

6. gain   lose   _____

7. gentle   tough   _____

8. ought   should not   _____

9. property   land   _____

10. question   ask   _____

11. slaughter   kill   _____

12. thaw   freeze   _____

4 More Work with Double Consonants. Draw a line between the double consonants, and mark the first vowel short. Then say the word out loud. Study the example before you begin.

1. hidden   *hĭd - den*   6. hitter   _____

2. clutter   _____   7. hobby   _____

3. bitten   _____   8. shatter   _____

4. wrapper   _____   9. trapper   _____

5. thinner   _____   10. common   _____

Review of *r*-Controlled Vowel Combinations

air	ear	eer	oar	oor	our
haircut	rear	sneer	soar	doorman	ours
stairway	dreary	sheer	uproar	doormat	ourselves
fairy	fear	cheer	board	floorboards	hourglass
fairly	beard	cheery	boardwalk	poorly	source
fairness	clearly	cheerful	cupboard	poorhouse	sourpuss
affair	yearly	cheerleader	keyboard	indoors	downpour

Words for Study

tow truck	grabbed	grasp	fluff
trespassing	piano	stumbled	holidays
giggled	disturbed	believe	unit

Mrs. Darkpill

At eight o'clock that Friday evening, Ginger had stopped by to pick up Tony. He hadn't told her where they were going. She hoped he had something planned that would make her feel more cheerful.

Ginger rang Tony's doorbell. The sky was full of storm clouds, and she felt certain it was going to pour. Sure enough, as she stood on the doormat, a downpour started. She dashed indoors, but she was already soaked.

Because of the dreary weather, Tony and Ginger decided to have a cup of coffee and listen to a few CDs before going out. Tony was telling Ginger about his crazy neighbor when the doorbell rang.

"Who would be out in such an awful downpour?" Ginger wondered.

Tony had barely opened the door when in barged Mrs. Darkpill with a sour look on her face. She didn't waste any time getting to the point.

"I thought you should know that I've called a tow truck," she sneered, "since your girlfriend decided to park her car in front of *my* driveway."

Ginger started to say she was sorry, but Tony cut her off. "Look, Mrs. Darkpill, I'll move Ginger's car right away, but if you don't get out of my house now, I'm going to call the cops and have you charged with trespassing!"

"How dare you threaten me!" screamed Mrs. Darkpill. "I'll sue you into the poorhouse if you're not careful!"

"Clearly you came over here just to start a fight," Tony said calmly. "I'm telling you to get out of my house. Why don't you go stand in the rain and cool off for a bit?"

At that, Ginger giggled. She couldn't help it. Tony shot her a warning look, but it was too late. Mrs. Darkpill whirled around to face her.

"Don't think I don't know who you are!" she shouted. "I know you have a boyfriend, and I know that you and Tony are having an affair!"

Now Ginger really started to laugh. She and Tony having an affair? How funny!

The laughter made Mrs. Darkpill even more angry. "I have my sources," she roared. "I watch everything that goes on around here!" Suddenly, in an act of sheer rage, she grabbed the coffee cup out of Ginger's hand and hurled it at the piano. The cup soared through the air and smashed into bits on the keyboard.

For the first time, Ginger felt some fear. Mrs. Darkpill was clearly disturbed. Things could get out of hand fairly quickly if she didn't calm down.

"Why don't we sit down and talk this whole thing over," Ginger said. She put her arm around Mrs. Darkpill and started to lead her over to the couch.

"Get your hands off me!" Mrs. Darkpill screamed. She tore loose from Ginger's grasp, knocking her off balance. Ginger stumbled into the cupboard. Cups, saucers, and plates shattered on the floorboards. Moments later, a police car roared into the driveway. The neighbors must have heard the uproar and called the cops.

"I don't believe this is happening," moaned Tony.

And that is how Ginger and Tony—and Mrs. Darkpill— happened to spend Friday night at the police station.

1 About the Story. Answer these questions.

1. Why did Tony and Ginger decide to have coffee and listen to CDs?

_____

2. What was the reason Mrs. Darkpill gave for being angry this time?

_____

3. What did Tony threaten to do to Mrs. Darkpill if she didn't leave?

_____

4. What did Tony say that made Ginger giggle?

_____

5. What made Ginger really start laughing?

_____

6. Why did Ginger try to calm Mrs. Darkpill down?

_____

What do you think?

7. Do you think the neighbors did the right thing by calling the police?

_____

8. Why do you think the police brought Tony, Ginger, and Mrs. Darkpill into the station?

_____

2 The _ea_ and _ee_ Words. Say the words in each group at the left out loud. Then fill in the blanks with the right answers.

dreary yearly cheery clearly	**1.** Every season comes round _____. Cold winter days help us think _____. The days are shorter and quite _____, But holidays make some folks _____.

seed sneeze weather feathers	**2.** Spring brings with it nicer _____. Birds wash and fluff their _____. People _____ and mow their lawns and others _____ from dusk till dawn.

sweat beaches sneer peaches	**3.** Some folks _____ at summer days. They hate to _____ and soak up rays. Others enjoy the sunny _____ and summer fruits like pears and _____.

breeze trees leaves sleeves	**4.** Fall brings out the pretty _____ that drop so gently from the _____. The days require longer _____, and soon folks feel a cooling _____.

cheer leap near year	**5.** Winter months are drawing _____, and snow will come by end of _____. Some folks _____ the holidays, others _____ on skis and sleighs.

reason clear least season	**6.** Everyone has their own good _____ for picking out a favorite _____. And some folks also make quite _____ their own _____ favorite time of year!

3 Syllables. A *syllable* is a word or part of a word said as a unit. For example, *near* has one syllable; *driveway* has two syllables; and *piano* has three syllables. Each of the words listed below has two syllables. Write these syllables on the line to the right of each word. Be sure to study the examples before you begin.

1. cardboard <u>card - board</u>

2. clearly <u>clear - ly</u>

3. cheerful _____

4. doughnut _____

5. fairly _____

6. uproar _____

7. floorboard _____

8. stairway _____

9. cobweb _____

10. fairness _____

11. downpour _____

12. invite _____

4 More Work with Units. Use the words below to fill in the blanks. Study the example before you begin.

feet	hours	letters
✓months	ounces	quarts
rooms	seconds	states

1. The 12 units of a year are called __*months*__ .

2. The 24 units of a day are called _____ .

3. The 60 units of a minute are called _____ .

4. The 4 units of a gallon are called _____ .

5. The 16 units of a pound are called _____ .

6. The 3 units of a yard are called _____ .

7. The units of the alphabet are called _____ .

8. The units inside a house are called _____ .

9. The units that make up the United States are called _____ .

Common Word Beginnings: Part 1

de-	ex-	mis-	com-	con-
describe	explain	mistake	complain	concern
decide	expect	mistaken	complaint	confront
deserve	excite	misplace	compose	contain
defend	explode	mistreat	combine	container
depend	except	misspell	compete	control
debate	exact	mistrust	complete	consume
destroy	exactly	miscount	completely	consumer
Detroit	excuse	misjudge	commit	consent

Words for Study

commented	yuck	ahead
vanilla	lemon	lazy
wisecracks	recipe	behave

Testing Recipes

Steven sat at the table in Holly's kitchen munching on peanut butter balls. "Not bad," he commented to Holly, who was trying to store the peanut butter balls in a container faster than Steven was eating them. "What's in them?"

"Rolled oats, milk, peanut butter, honey, salt, vanilla, and chopped nuts," answered Holly. "Enough of the peanut butter balls. Now try some of this." She pushed a bowl in front of Steven.

"What is it?" asked Steven. "It looks exactly like baby food—after the baby has spit it out."

"Why don't you decide what it's like after you taste it?" laughed Holly. "I'm never going to get this cookbook ready with food experts like you making wisecracks all the time."

"Yuck! Holly, this is awful. It's prunes. I hate prunes!"

"Prune whip to be exact," said Holly. "Prunes combined with lemon juice, honey, and egg whites. Very good for what ails you."

"Nothing is ailing me except this awful taste in my mouth," replied Steven. "If I were you, I'd destroy this recipe at once. Let me test the peanut butter balls again."

"Is the prune whip really that bad?"

"Here," said Steven, "go ahead and try some. Be my guest."

"Well," said Holly after trying a spoonful, "I'm not going to debate with you on this one," and she tore up the recipe card. As she checked the two pans of date-nut bread in the oven, she asked, "How's Jerome doing? Does he still think the world's giving him a raw deal?"

"He's a little better," responded Steven. "What's crazy is that he found out why Ginger never made it to the party, and he still won't call her."

"As far as I'm concerned," said Holly, "Jerome is one of those men who will never commit himself to doing the things you have to do in order to get what you want in life. Then he spends all his time complaining about how other people let you down or are lazy or dumb."

"You're being a bit hard on him, aren't you?" asked Steven. "He's not down on other people. It's just that he has these silly rules about how people should behave, and he can't see that the rules might have been good at one time, but they're kind of useless now. Jerome's a very complex person, Holly. It's not really fair of you to judge him like that."

"I'm not judging him," exclaimed Holly. "I'm just telling you what I see."

"Well," grinned Steven, "let me tell you what I see. I see smoke coming out of the oven."

"Oh, no!" groaned Holly. "The date-nut bread! I completely forgot about it!"

1 About the Story. Answer these questions.

1. List three recipes that Holly was testing.

   a. _____

   b. _____

   c. _____

2. Why was Holly testing these recipes?

   _____

3. Which recipe did Steven think was good? _____

4. Which recipe did Steven think was awful? _____

5. What did Holly think Jerome's problem was?

   _____

6. What did Steven think Jerome's problem was?

   _____

7. What happened to the third recipe that Holly was testing?

_____

What do you think?

8. Who do you think is right about Jerome—Holly or Steven? Be sure to explain your answer.

_____

_____

9. Which of Holly's recipes would you enjoy the most?

_____

2 Sounds for _ow._ Fill in the blanks with the words below.

bowl	cow	flowerpot	rowboat
bowling	downstream	grown-ups	shower
brownie	elbow	pillow	towel rack

_____ **1.** This word is a container for plants.

_____ **2.** This is a game in which you try for strikes and spares.

_____ **3.** You find this in the bathroom next to the sink or tub.

_____ **4.** This is a dish for serving oatmeal or prune whip.

_____ **5.** This is the way a river flows.

_____ **6.** This is a chocolate treat.

_____ **7.** Many people put their heads on this when they go to sleep.

_____ **8.** This is the joint or bend of the arm.

_____ **9.** This is where you go to get cleaned up.

_____ **10.** This is what most children call older people.

_____ **11.** You need a pair of oars to get across a lake in this.

_____ **12.** You'll find this animal in a herd in a field or on the range.

3 More Work with Syllables. In the box below are some syllables that you can use to make words. The words will fit the eight sentences. No syllable is used twice, and no syllables should be left over when you are done. The number after the sentence tells you how many syllables are in each word. Study the example before you begin.

au	bor	Cin	~~day~~	dro	hel	i	laun	mat	neigh	re	ter	to
biles	ci	cop	der	el	hood	la	ly	mo	pe	~~ter~~	tight	~~yes~~

<u>yesterday</u>   **1.** This is what the day before today is called. (3)

_____ **2.** These are what most people drive. (4)

_____ **3.** This is the name of a girl in a fairy tale who lost her slipper at the prince's ball. (4)

_____ **4.** This machine flies in the sky and can land on the top of buildings. (4)

_____ **5.** This is where some people go to wash their clothes. (3)

_____ **6.** This instructs a cook in how to make a certain food. (3)

_____ **7.** If you have a good grip on something, this is how you are holding it. (2)

_____ **8.** This word describes the streets near your home. (3)

4 Brain Benders. Do you know what the experts tell us about food? Answer *true* or *false* to these ten sentences. (If you don't know the answer, make a good guess.)

_____ **1.** Whole grain bread is better for you than white bread.

_____ **2.** It's not important to wash fresh fruits and vegetables.

_____ **3.** Low-fat milk is part of a healthy diet.

_____ **4.** You don't have to put leftovers in the refrigerator.

_____ **5.** Raw eggs are good for you.

_____ **6.** Healthy protein choices are lean beef, skinless chicken, and beans.

_____ **7.** People do not need to exercise every day.

_____ **8.** A good diet is high in fat and sugar.

_____ **9.** You can check the temperature to see if cooked meat is safe to eat.

_____ **10.** The food you eat has nothing to do with how you feel.

Word Index: Lessons 1–16

A

actor
adult
advice
affair
afford
afterward
agree
ahead
ahoy
aim
aloud
already
although
anymore
anyone
apart
apartment
ape
appear
armful
arrest
arrive
aside
August
auto
automobile
autumn
avoid

B

backfire
background
backpack
bait
balance
barber
barge
bathing
bathtub
bead
beard
beast
beaten
bedding
beg
beginning
behave
believe

bench
berserk
besides
bin
binge
birch
bitten
blackboard
blade
blank
blast
blend
blessing
blindly
blond
bloody
bloom
blues
blurt
boardwalk
boast
boiler
bookcase
bookshelf
bookworm
boom
border
borrow
bother
bottom
bound
bowl
bowling
brace
bracelet
brag
braid
brainy
branch
breast
breed
breeze
bribe
broil
broken
brook
brownie
bruise
brush
bucket

building
bulk
bulky
Butch
buzz

C

camper
camping
cannot
cardboard
carpenter
carpet
caution
cautious
CD
certainly
chalk
chalkboard
cheapskate
cheat
cheer
cheerful
cheerleader
cheery
chestnut
chilly
chin
chirp
chore
chose
chow
chunk
cider
cinch
cinder
Cinderella
circle
circus
clam
clammy
clash
clearing
clearly
clench
clerk
cling
clingy
clothing

clumsy
clung
clutch
clutter
cob
cobweb
cockroach
cocoa
coconut
coffeecake
colt
combination
combine
comeback
coming
comment
commit
commonly
compete
complain
complaint
complete
completely
compose
concern
concert
confront
confuse
confusing
consent
consonant
consume
consumer
contain
container
control
convince
cord
cork
corner
corpse
costly
cough
counter
countless
courtroom
cove
covering
cramp
crate

crick
cringe
crosswalk
crow
crude
cruise
cruiser
crutch
crybaby
Cuban
cuff
cupboard
cure
cutting

D

daily
Darkpill
darn
daughter
daybreak
daydream
deadline
debate
deepen
defend
delete
dense
dentist
depend
despair
despite
destroy
Detroit
diet
difference
dill
dishpan
dishrag
dishwasher
disturb
diver
doggy
dome
doorbell
doorknob
doorman
doormat
dose

dough
doughnut
downpour
drape
drawn
dread
dreadful
dreamer
dreamland
dreary
drench
dresser
dressing
drift
drill
drip
driven
driveway
drug
drugstore
dryer
dunce

E

earring
ease
eaten
e-card
edge
edgy
elbow
elf
elk
e-mail
enjoy
enter
etc.
eve
exact
exactly
except
excite
exclaim
excuse
exercise
expect
explode
eyesight
eyestrain

F

fairly
fairness
fairy
faith
faithful
fallen
family
fancy
farther
fate
faucet
fault
faulty
favorite
feast
feather
figure
filter
finger
fingernail
fingerprint
fir
firelight
fisherman
fitting
flail
flap
flashlight
flea
flight
flighty
flirt
floorboard
flowerpot
fluff
flute
folk(s)
footing
footprint
forbid
force
forge
forgive
forgiven
forgotten
forth
freeway
freight

freshly
fright
frighten
frog
frown
frozen
fur
further

G

gag
Gail
gain
gale
gall
garlic
gauze
gaze
gear
gee
geese
gem
gentle
gentleman
gently
giggle
given
glance
glee
globe
gloom
gloomy
glove
glumly
gnarled
gnash
gnat
gnaw
gnawing
gnome
gob
gobble
golf
goodies
goof
goofy
gorge
gosh
grab

Grace
grace
grandfather
grandmother
grapevine
grasp
grease
greedy
greet
grief
gross
grouchy
growl
grudge
grumpy
grungy
gulf
gull
gully
gumdrop
gust
gut
gutter

H

habit
hail
hairbrush
hairy
handshake
happiness
harass
hardware
harp
haul
haunt
haunted
headache
health food
height
hem
Herb
herb
highway
hip-hop
hoist
holder
holiday
Holly

homemade
homesick
homey
hotel
hourglass
hourly
how's
hurl
hush

I

icing
improve
indoors
indulge
insist
instruct
invite
involve
iron
ivy

J

jelly
Jerome
jet
Joyce
joyful
judge
juice
juicy
jumpy
jury

K

keyboard
kin
kinfolk(s)
Kirk
kitchen
knack
knapsack
knee-deep
knelt
knight
knob
knockout
knotting
knotty

L

lampshade
lance
lard
lately
latest
laughter
laundromat
laundry
lawyer
lazy
leaky
leap
leapfrog
leash
leather
ledge
Lee
leftover
lemon
lesson
lifeguard
lighten
lighter
lighthouse
lining
listen
lively
lodge
loose
loosen
lousy
lower
low-fat
loyally
loyalty
Luke
lukewarm
lunge
lurch

M

machine
madly
mailbox
mailman
malt
manager
mankind

Mansfield
Martin
mash
matchbook
merge
message
mighty
Miguel
milkshake
mince
mincemeat
miscount
misjudge
misplace
misspell
mist
mistaken
mistreat
mistrust
moan
moist
moisten
mold
moldy
moment
moose
mope
motel
movement
murder
murmur
muscle
music

N

nasty
naughty
nearby
neatly
neighbor
neighborhood
neither
nervous
newspaper
newsstand
nook
nor
notch
notice

nudge

O

oak
oat
oatmeal
oddly
ooze
ought
ours
ourselves
overboard
overdone
overgrown
overnight
owe
ox

P

pact
padding
painful
painless
paperback
parent
paste
patty
Paul
pause
pave
paving
peacefully
peanut
perch
perform
perk
piano
pigpen
pillow
pinch
pitch
pitcher
pitchfork
plainly
player
playground
plea
plead
pleasant

pleased
pledge
plenty
plow
plump
plunge
poach
poorhouse
poorly
porch
pose
pounce
pout
practice
praise
prance
prank
press
pretty
prince
probably
promise
prop
proper
properly
property
protein
pry
puffy
putty

Q

quarrel
quarter

R

racecourse
raft
rag
railroad
rainy
rarely
rash
ray
rear
recall
recipe
recover
refresh

reject
rejection
rejoice
remark
repair
repeat
reply
reporter
require
respect
respond
restless
retire
retreat
reveal
ridden
ridge
rinse
risky
roadwork
roller
Rome
roof
rotten
rough
route
rowboat
royally
royalty
rut
Ruth

S

salsa
salty
Sam
sandwich
saucepan
saucer
savings
scald
scale
scary
scheme
scold
scoop
scorch
scoreboard
Scotch

Scott
scour
scram
scraper
scratchy
screw
script
scroll
scrounge
scruff
season
seaweed
serving
shade
shady
shaken
shark
she'd
sheer
shelf
shelter
she's
shipwreck
shootout
shopping
shortcake
shorts
shoulder
shove
shown
shy
shyly
sideshow
sidewalk
sift
silk
silky
sill
single
sir
skater
sketch
ski
skid
skillful
skinless
skinny
skip
skull
slaughter

sled
sleepover
sleet
sleigh
slept
slid
slide
slight
slot
slouch
slump
smack
smear
Smith
smog
smoky
smooth
smoothly
smudge
snarl
snatch
sneak
sneakers
sneaky
sneer
sniff
snowball
snowstorm
snowy
soar
softly
sole
son
sooner
sought
source
sourpuss
spaceship
spaghetti
span
spark
special
speck
sped
speech
spendthrift
spied
spine
spit
splurge

spoken
spoonful
spy
square
squarely
squirm
stairway
standstill
starch
starfish
stash
station
steel
stem
Steve
Steven
stew
stir
stitch
stocking
stony
stool
stoop
stork
straighten
stray
streak
stress
stressful
stretch
stretchy
stuffing
stuffy
stumble
stunt
subject
successfully
suit
suitcase
sulk
sulky
sunken
sunless
suppose
swam
Swede
Sweden
sweep
sweeper
swept

Swiss
syllable
system

T

tag
tailspin
tasteless
tasty
taught
Ted
tee
teepee
tennis
tense
Thanksgiving
theft
themselves
they're
thickly
thief
thinner
thirst
thirsty
thorn
thread
threaten
thrift
thrifty
thrill
throat
throughout
thud
thump
tighten
tightly
till
tilt
together
toil
Tony
toolbox
toothbrush
toothpaste
tough
tow
tow truck
trace
trainer

trance
tread
trend
trespass
tribe
tricky
troll
troop
trooper
trousers
trout
truce
trudge
truthfully

U

underground
undershirt
understand
understood
unhealthy
unit
uproar
urge

V

vane
vanilla
veal
verge
video
vine
visit
voice mail
void
volt
vow

W

waist
waistline
waiter
waitress
wallet
Walter
waltz
wander
warmer
washcloth

washing
wastebasket
watchman
weaken
weather
website
wedding
weight
we'll
well-done
weren't
whack
wham
whatsoever
wheeze
whether
whichever
whim
whine
who's
wildly
William
wilt
window
wise
wisecrack
wisely
woods
workout
workshop
wrapper
wrapping
wrecker
wren
wrench
wring
wrung

X

Y

yeah
yearly
YMCA
yoga
you'll
you've
yuck

Z

Common Word Beginnings: Part 2

de-	ex-	com-	con-	un-
define	expose	command	conclude	unclear
defeat	extend	commander	confess	undo
delight	extent	commandment	confide	undid
devote	extreme	composer	confine	unfit
demand	extremely	composed	conceal	unwilling
decay	express	compare	convince	unlikely
declare	explore	compute	construct	uncover
detach	explorer	comply	conform	uncertain

Words for Study

alarm	flu	slacks	whoever
Dennis	desire	comforted	hurry
afraid	shoppers	booth	quiet

Tony's Day Off

When the alarm clock rang, Tony shut it off, rolled over, and tried to go back to sleep. He was just about asleep when he remembered that he had to call in sick. If he failed to comply with this rule, his boss would dock him a day's pay. He looked up the number of Mr. Dennis, his boss, in his cell phone. The phone rang six times before Mr. Dennis answered it.

"Yeah, what do you want?" said Mr. Dennis in an extremely unfriendly voice.

Tony made his voice sound as weak as he could. He was afraid that Mr. Dennis would guess that he wasn't really sick. "Hi, it's Tony. I think I'm coming down with the flu. Is it okay with you if I take the day off and rest?"

"Who do you think I am, your mother?" exploded Mr. Dennis. "You know very well you've got fifteen sick days a year. If you're sick, you take a sick day. Is that so hard to figure out?"

"I just wanted to check it out," replied Tony, who was having trouble concealing his desire to tell his boss off.

The minute Tony hung up the phone, he felt great. As he took his shower, he made up a little song about Mr. Dennis. The song amused him so much that he cut himself in three places while shaving because he was laughing so hard.

He treated himself to a huge breakfast of grapefruit juice, fried eggs, ham, toast, doughnuts, and coffee at a nearby diner. As he was having his second cup of coffee, he saw an ad in the newspaper for a great clothing sale at a men's store only three blocks from the diner.

It seemed as if every man in town had the same idea because the store was filled with shoppers by the time Tony got there. He had to fight his way to the racks, but he was comforted when he saw how cheap the clothing was compared to other stores in town. He chose two pairs of slacks and a brown sweater to try on.

Tony waited in line to use the fitting booth for what seemed like an hour. "Whoever you are, will you please hurry up in there," commanded Tony. "I haven't got all day, you know."

All at once, it became very quiet in the fitting booth, "Oh, yeah? That's what you think. You'll have all the time in the world to shop for fancy clothes now, Tony," declared Mr. Dennis as he poked his head from behind the curtain, "because you're fired!"

1 About the Story. Answer these questions.

1. In what three places does this story take place?

    a. _____

    b. _____

    c. _____

2. Who is Tony's boss? _____

3. What kind of mood is Tony's boss in when Tony calls him up? _____

4. Why does Tony say he can't go to work? _____

5. What does Tony decide to do after breakfast? _____

6. Why does Tony lose his job?

_____

What do you think?

7. If you were Tony, what would you have said to Mr. Dennis when you saw him in the store?

_____

_____

8. Do you think Mr. Dennis will change his mind about firing Tony?

_____

_____

2 More Work with the Sounds for *ow*. To find the answers, choose a word from **List A** and add a word from **List B** to it. Write the compound word on the line.

List A	List B
blow	bar
break	case
crow	crows
down	down
land	flow
over	flowers
pillow	out
scare	owner
slow	people
snow	plow
towns	poke
wild	pour

_____ 1. This is an iron bar used to move or lift things.

_____ 2. This person has property.

_____ 3. This word describes something that bursts quickly, such as a car tire.

_____ 4. This is used to clear the roads after a winter storm.

_____ 5. This person moves very slowly.

_____ 6. This word describes those who live in a city.

_____ 7. This word describes a heavy rain.

_____ 8. People enjoy picking these on walks through the woods or fields.

_____ 9. This covers the pad you rest your head on when you sleep.

_____ 10. Farmers put these in their fields to help keep birds from eating their crops.

_____ 11. What you call it when your auto completely stops working.

_____ 12. When something is filled past what it can hold, you have this.

3 Which Word Does Not Fit? On the line to the right, write the word that does not fit with the rest.

1. grapefruit   lemon   peach   pear   peas   _____

2. caring   gentle   kind   loving   unfriendly   _____

3. cheek   chin   eyes   knees   mouth   _____

4. brush   comb   lipstick   mirror   purse   _____

5. bold   brave   daring   tough   weak   _____

6. all wet   drenched   dripping   rain   soaked   _____

7. hunted   looked for   searched   shelter   sought   _____

8. go fast   hurry   relax   rush   speed   _____

9. calm   composed   nervous   peaceful   relaxed   _____

10. build   compose   construct   destroy   make   _____

11. conceal   expose   reveal   show   uncover   _____

12. comment   declare   express   mute   speak   _____

4 More Work with Syllables. Say each word out loud. On the lines to the right of each word, write the syllables you hear. Study the examples before you begin.

1. confess   _con_ • _fess_

2. booth   _booth_

3. extreme   _ex_ • _treme_

4. extremely _____ • _____ • _____

5. shopper _____ • _____

6. flu   _____

7. sixteen _____ • _____

8. yesterday _____ • _____ • _____

9. winner _____ • _____

10. payday _____ • _____

11. homesick _____ • _____

12. restroom _____ • _____

13. overboard _____ • _____ • _____

14. unfriendly _____ • _____ • _____

15. basketball _____ • _____ • _____

Common Word Beginnings: Part 3

ex-	dis-	un-	im-	in-
exchange	discuss	uncooked	impress	income
exceed	disgust	unlawful	improve	increase
expand	display	unpack	impose	insect
expense	dispose	unpaid	impure	insight
expel	discharge	untrained	import	injure
exist	discover	unafraid	imported	injury
exhaust	discovery	uneven	improper	inquire
exert	disturb	uneasy	improperly	intend

Words for Study

admit	harsh	hasn't
you'd	limit	garbage
universe	disagree	extra

A Talk with Jerome

"The trouble with you, Jerome," said Steven, "is that you can't admit you've made a mistake. Why don't you just admit to yourself how much you'd really like to get together with Ginger again and then do what you have to do in order to get things straightened out? Instead you mope around as if nobody else exists in the universe but you."

Jerome felt that Steven was being too harsh with him, but he was so exhausted from feeling awful that he didn't say a word.

"You know," Steven went on, "there's a limit to just how much you can expect from other people. If you want something bad enough, you're the one who has to go after it. As my mom used to tell me when I was a kid, the world doesn't owe you anything. And she's right, Jerome. Nobody owes you a thing. It's a hard fact to learn, but it's true."

"I disagree with you there," replied Jerome in a sad voice. "If Ginger wanted to see me, why hasn't she called me?"

"You're missing the whole point," said Steven who was starting to feel disgusted with the way Jerome refused to face his problem. "The point is that you have to do something to get what you want out of life. Forget all this garbage about what other people should do. That kind of thinking will just drive you crazy. You have to think about what you should be doing for yourself."

"So you think I should call her?" asked Jerome after a long pause.

"Yeah. If you want to see her, call her and tell her that," replied Steven as he went into the kitchen to get himself something to drink.

"What if she doesn't want to see me?" yelled Jerome.

"That's a chance you have to take. The important thing," explained Steven, "is that you'd be doing something instead of waiting around for somebody else to do it for you. Just doing something will make you feel a lot better. Anyway, she must want to see you. Tony told you that she was upset when she found out she missed your party." Steven was beginning to feel as if he were talking to a child.

"What if she really started the fight with Tony's nutty neighbor just to get out of coming to the party?" Jerome whined.

Steven slammed the refrigerator door shut in disgust. "Jerome, Tony didn't even mention the party to Ginger until they were driving home from the police station. I really can't talk about this anymore. Either call her or don't call her, but don't come complaining to me anymore. I'm sick of it. I just don't want to hear it."

"So why didn't they come to the party after they got out of the police station?" Jerome inquired.

"JEROME! I said I don't want to hear it!"

"Okay, okay," said Jerome.

"Okay, what?" Steven inquired.

"Okay, so I'll call her!"

1 About the Story. Answer these questions.

1. What does Steven think is the matter with Jerome at the beginning of the story?

_____

_____

2. What point is Steven trying to get Jerome to understand? _____

_____

3. Why does Jerome think that Ginger might have started the fight with Tony's neighbor?

_____

_____

4. Why does Steven get so angry with Jerome? _____

_____

5. At the end of the story, does Jerome decide that Steven is right or wrong? How do you know?

_____

_____

2 Short Stories. Fill in the blanks with the right choices from the word groups at the left.

convince
disagreed
discussed
expands
extra

1. In class yesterday, the teacher _____ how water _____ when it is heated. Andy _____ with this, and the teacher spent an _____ ten minutes after class trying to _____ him of the truth of this fact.

exceeding
exchanged
extra
unfriendly
unfit

2. The policeman pulled Mr. Jones over to the side of the road for _____ the speed limit. The two men _____ angry words. In a very _____ voice, Mr. Jones told the policeman that he was _____ for this job. The policeman hoped the court would fine him an _____ twenty bucks for being so rude.

expenses
exhausted
income
uncertain
unhealthy

3. Mary was so _____ when she got home from work that she was _____ how long she could keep two jobs and still take care of an apartment and two children. She knew that working this hard was _____, but she had so many _____ that she needed the _____ from two jobs just to make ends meet.

3 Spelling Check. The answers to the clues are listed at the left. As you can see, the letters of the words are all mixed up. Spell the words the right way on the lines.

b h m t u

1. _____ Little children suck this when they're upset or bored.

A g s t u u

2. _____ This is the eighth month of the year.

a e l l w t

3. _____ People keep money, pictures, and important papers in this.

| a c c e h k p y | **4.** _____ | A worker gets this each week or every other week for his work. |

| a o o p t t | **5.** _____ | You can bake, boil, fry, or mash this for your dinner. |

| a C d e e i l l n r | **6.** _____ | A fairy godmother helped her get to a ball where she waltzed with Prince Charming until the clock struck twelve. |

| a l t w z | **7.** _____ | This is the kind of dancing that Prince Charming and Answer 6 did at the ball. |

| r e d e c l e a h r e | **8.** _____ | This is a person who shouts to the crowd and urges a team to win. |

4 More Words That Begin with *in-*. Use the words below to fill in the blanks. Use the rules you have learned to sound out the new words.

infect	inhale	instruct	invent
inform	inspire	invade	invite

_____ **1.** to draw air into the lungs

_____ **2.** to make a machine or anything else brand-new

_____ **3.** to tell or report something to someone

_____ **4.** to take over another person's land by force

_____ **5.** to ask someone to come to your house

_____ **6.** to teach someone how to do something

_____ **7.** to give someone germs that will make them sick

_____ **8.** to fill someone with hope

Up-, Down-, Out-, Over-, and Under-

up-	down-	out-	over-	under-
update	downhill	outlook	overcoat	undershirt
upscale	downfall	outcome	overhead	underground
upbeat	downright	outdoors	overtime	underdog
uptown	downstream	outsmart	overnight	understood
upkeep	downcast	outskirts	overcome	undertaker
upstairs	downstairs	outspoken	overflow	underwear
upside-down	downhearted	outstanding	overseas	underneath
upcoming	down-to-earth	outnumber	overweight	understated

Holidays

New Year's Eve
New Year's Day
Valentine's Day
April Fool's Day
Fourth of July
Halloween
Thanksgiving
Christmas

Months of the Year

January	July
February	August
March	September
April	October
May	November
June	December

Words for Study

café	staff	weeknight
slipper	area	huh
brighter	balcony	continue

Jerome and Ginger

Jerome decided that he would not call Ginger after all. He would go see her in person. Checking through the newspaper, he saw that Ginger was singing at a new café that had just opened uptown. The café was called The Glass Slipper. Jerome felt this was a lucky sign. As he was putting on his overcoat, he found himself humming one of the first songs that Ginger had ever written. Steven had been right. Now that Jerome had decided to act, he no longer felt downcast. In fact, he felt upbeat, and even his outlook for the future seemed brighter.

The café was very upscale, with a small stage and fancy overhead lighting, but the staff seemed down-to-earth and friendly. There was an outdoor seating area and an upstairs balcony. But since it was winter and a weeknight, there were only a few people in the café.

Jerome spotted Ginger, sitting next to the piano player. She wasn't singing, so she must be on break, he thought. Jerome was overcome by how lovely Ginger looked and suddenly understood just how much he had missed her.

Ginger must have felt Jerome's stare, for at that very moment, she looked up from the keyboard and gazed right into Jerome's eyes. It would have been clear to anybody watching that both Ginger and Jerome were overcome with strong feelings. Ginger murmured something to the piano player, got up, and walked slowly over to Jerome's table.

"Hello, Jerome," she said shyly.

"Hi, Ginger." Jerome sounded as nervous as he felt. "How have you been?"

"I'm okay. What brought you up here on this dark, chilly night?" Ginger asked.

"Oh, I just felt like hearing 'September Song' and I didn't have any plans for this evening, so I thought I'd come on up here and ask you to sing it for me," Jerome lied.

"You always said that 'September Song' bored you!" exclaimed Ginger.

"That's not true!" Jerome said. "It is understated, but that's the best thing about it."

"Look, Jerome, why are you really here? You always claim that people should be outspoken and not beat around the bush, but that's exactly what I think you're doing right now."

"Are you going to sing 'September Song'?"

"Jerome," threatened Ginger, "I'm going to give you just one more chance to explain what you're doing here."

"Maybe I was right about your mean streak," Jerome joked. "I guess you haven't been practicing yoga after all, huh?"

"Jerome, this is going downhill quickly. If all you want to do is continue our fight, then we're done talking," Ginger said. She turned to walk away.

"Wait, Ginger. I was just making a dumb joke. I guess that's part of the problem. I've been doing a lot of thinking, and I want you to know that underneath all my jokes and smart remarks, I miss you very much."

Ginger said nothing. She touched Jerome gently on the cheek and turned to go back to the band. "Hey!" shouted Jerome. "I'm sorry! Where are you going?"

"To sing 'September Song,'" Ginger replied softly. Jerome felt so happy, he thought his heart would overflow.

1 About the Story. Answer these questions.

1. Why does Jerome decide not to call up Ginger?

_____

2. Where does most of this story take place?

_____

3. What is Ginger doing when Jerome first sees her?

_____

4. What reason does Jerome first give Ginger for coming to see her?

_____

5. What does Jerome do that almost makes Ginger walk away?

_____

6. How do you know that Ginger has forgiven Jerome by the end of the story?

_____

What do you think?

7. Why does Jerome think it's a lucky sign that the café is called The Glass Slipper?

_____

_____

2 Twelve Questions. Write the underlined word that is correct on the line to the left.

_____ 1. In most houses, are the bedrooms <u>downstairs</u> or <u>upstairs</u>?

_____ 2. If it's raining hard outside, do children play <u>indoors</u> or <u>outdoors</u>?

_____ 3. Does a happy person feel <u>upbeat</u> or <u>downcast</u>?

_____ 4. Is the money that you earn called your <u>income</u> or your <u>outcome</u>?

_____ 5. When you take out the trash, are you <u>composing</u> or <u>disposing</u> of it?

_____ 6. If you broil a steak for a long time, is it <u>overdone</u> or <u>uncooked</u>?

_____ 7. When you report a rude waiter to his or her manager, are you <u>complaining</u> or <u>explaining</u>?

_____   **8.** When you ask someone to do too much to help you, are you <u>imposing</u> or <u>exposing</u>?

_____   **9.** If a person gets better after a long illness, has the person <u>recovered</u> or <u>uncovered</u>?

_____   **10.** If you tell your boss that you refuse to do something that you've been ordered to do, are you <u>complying</u> or <u>replying</u>?

_____   **11.** If you go along with what everyone else does, are you <u>reforming</u> or <u>conforming</u>?

_____   **12.** If a person forgets his or her name, is the person <u>refused</u> or <u>confused</u>?

3 The Four Seasons. Put each word below under the best heading.

March	August	beach	New Year's Eve
Halloween	hot weather	falling leaves	flowers blooming
December	ice skating	October	schools open
snowstorms	spring training	April Fool's Day	Fourth of July

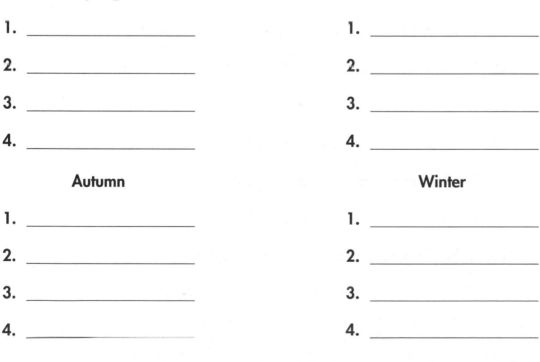

Spring

1. _____

2. _____

3. _____

4. _____

Summer

1. _____

2. _____

3. _____

4. _____

Autumn

1. _____

2. _____

3. _____

4. _____

Winter

1. _____

2. _____

3. _____

4. _____

4 The Months of the Year. Do you remember this verse?

> Thirty days has September,
> April, June, and November.
> When short February is done,
> All the rest have thirty-one.

Use the list of months to fill in the blanks. You may need to use a word more than once.

| January | March | May | July | September | November |
| February | April | June | August | October | December |

_____ **1.** In what month is New Year's Day?

_____ **2.** In what month is New Year's Eve?

_____ **3.** In what month is Halloween?

_____ **4.** In what month is Thanksgiving?

_____ **5.** In what month is Valentine's Day?

_____ **6.** In what month is Christmas?

_____ **7.** We celebrate on the fourth day of this month.

_____ **8.** In what month do most children get out of school?

_____ **9.** In what month do most children return to school?

_____ **10.** In what month is your birthday?

_____ **11.** In what month does spring begin?

_____ **12.** In what month does summer begin?

_____ **13.** In what month does autumn begin?

_____ **14.** In what month does winter begin?

_____ **15.** Which month of the year do you like the most?

_____ **16.** Which month of the year do you like the least?

More Work with Compound Words

dipstick	widespread	teaspoon	blacksmith
bookmark	bedspread	tablespoon	blackmail
landmark	bedtime	tablecloth	slowpoke
landlord	mealtime	clothesline	slowdown
landlady	password	clothespin	sundown
homeland	passport	hairpin	sunrise
homebody	ringside	hairbrush	heartbeat
housework	seaport	paintbrush	heartbreak
courthouse	seacoast	horseback	breakdown
farmhouse	seafood	horseplay	breakthrough

Words for Study

contract	honor	kidding	included
publisher	beautiful	matchmaker	different
bookstores	dessert	midnight	deny

Holly's Book Party

Holly decided to throw a party. She had just signed a contract that morning for her book, and the publisher had told her that her health food cookbook would be on the shelves of all the well-known bookstores and health food stores by February.

By early afternoon, she had invited the whole yoga class, Jerome and Ginger, Gail, Tony, and a few other friends to the party. Because Steven had been so helpful in testing the recipes, she told him he was to be her guest of honor.

When Jerome called Holly to thank her for inviting him, he asked her if she was going to serve real food or health food. Holly just laughed and told him that she was so sick of all the recipes in her cookbook that she had already planned to serve a spaghetti dinner. "In that case" said Jerome, "you can count on me to help with the dishes. Can I bring anything?"

"Bring some wine," Holly replied. "And, if you don't mind, call Tony and tell him to bring some, too. I've got to start making the tomato sauce right now if everything is going to be ready on time."

The party was a huge success. Holly looked beautiful in a red dress that she had rushed out to buy between making the tomato sauce and baking the cheesecake. Everyone was happy for her success as a cookbook writer.

Just as a gag, Holly brought out a large glass bowl of prune whip for dessert. She placed it on the tablecloth and handed Steven a teaspoon.

"Steven, to thank you for all your help, you get the honor of the first bite," Holly said.

Steven turned pale and wondered if Holly's feelings would be hurt if he refused to eat the dessert. He stood there, holding the spoon, not knowing what to do. Holly couldn't help laughing when she saw the look on his face.

"Just kidding," grinned Holly. "The real desserts are in the kitchen."

"Now I know why they call a joke a gag," Steven remarked, looking at the awful prune whip.

Jerome watched Steven and Holly joke around together. It seemed clear to him that the two of them would end up dating soon. They would make a good match, Jerome thought. He had been playing matchmaker for his friends ever since he and Ginger had patched things up. Jerome felt that everyone deserved to be as happy as he was at that moment.

Ginger arrived at Holly's apartment around midnight because her boss let her leave work early. She had never met Holly before, and she was glad to be included. The two women liked each other at once. Ginger also enjoyed meeting all the people from the yoga class and asked all sorts of questions about yoga.

Jerome could tell from how excited Ginger was that by next week, both he and Ginger would be down at the YMCA trying to stand on their heads. He didn't mind. He remembered his own party and how bad he had felt. It all seemed like a long time ago, even though it really wasn't. Now, here he was, feeling so happy, with Ginger by his side and his third plate of chocolate cheesecake in his hand.

"That's life," he thought to himself as he kissed Ginger on the cheek. "One minute you're down, and the next minute you're up. You just never know what's going to happen next!"

1 About the Story. Answer these questions.

1. Why is Holly throwing a party?

_____

2. What does Jerome ask Holly when he calls her to thank her for inviting him?

_____

3. Why has Holly planned to serve a spaghetti dinner?

_____

4. Why does Holly make Steven her guest of honor?

_____

5. What does Holly serve for dessert as a gag?

_____

6. What is the real dessert?

_____

7. What does Jerome think will happen with Holly and Steven in the future?

_____

8. What does Jerome think he and Ginger will be doing next week?

_____

9. How does Jerome seem different in this story?

_____

10. What does Jerome seem to have learned about life?

_____

_____

2 More Work with Compound Words. Choose the right word from the four choices, and write the letter on the line to the left.

_____ **1.** Sometimes you have to show this in order to enter another country.

a. homeland   b. passport   c. bookmark   d. password

_____ **2.** When you lose someone you love, you feel this.

a. heartbeat   b. breakthrough   c. breakdown   d. heartbreak

_____ **3.** This person is most happy when he is in his own home.

a. anybody   b. busybody   c. homebody   d. somebody

_____ **4.** This is the time right before evening.

a. sunrise   b. sundown   c. sunlight   d. Sunday

_____ **5.** This is another word for your spine.

    a. backbone   b. backfire   c. background   d. comeback

_____ **6.** This is a common thing to buy for the Fourth of July.

    a. firelight   b. firecracker   c. backfire   d. fireplace

_____ **7.** This is when you go to sleep.

    a. lifetime   b. overtime   c. mealtime   d. bedtime

_____ **8.** This is a place for people who have no money.

    a. lighthouse   b. farmhouse   c. poorhouse   d. courthouse

_____ **9.** This is the country you were born in.

    a. homesick   b. homemade   c. homework   d. homeland

_____ **10.** This person is not fast.

    a. slowpoke   b. slowdown   c. downpour   d. slowly

3 Words That Mean the Same. Choose the word from the line that means the same thing as the first word, and write it on the line to the right. Study the example before you begin.

1. **discover:**	conceal	cover	find	lose	_find_
2. **exhausted:**	asleep	relaxed	awake	tired	_____
3. **heavy:**	slim	skinny	overweight	thin	_____
4. **barely:**	hardly	unlikely	not at all	clearly	_____
5. **thrown:**	baseball	caught	catch	hurled	_____
6. **harsh:**	calm	mild	rough	rude	_____
7. **fancy:**	plain	ugly	upscale	pretty	_____
8. **chilly:**	coldly	warmly	mild	cold	_____
9. **kidding:**	joking	playing	playground	joker	_____
10. **sulk:**	plead	prance	praise	pout	_____

4 Word Opposites. Choose the word from the line that means the opposite of the first word, and write it on the line to the right. Study the example before you begin.

1. **male:**   mother   daughter   female   lady   <u>*female*</u>

2. **sweet:**   awful   honey   sour   sugar   _____

3. **future:**   over   old   past   before   _____

4. **honor:**   shame   praise   lie   fault   _____

5. **thaw:**   freeze   liquid   melt   solid   _____

6. **injure:**   hurt   health   heel   heal   _____

7. **admit:**   confess   deny   disagree   confide   _____

8. **pale:**   flash   flashed   flesh   flushed   _____

9. **not sure:**   certain   uncertain   convince   doubt   _____

10. **expand:**   conform   conclude   confide   contract   _____

5 Feelings. How do you think the people in these little stories feel? Choose your answer from the four choices, and write it on the line. Then, on the line below the story, explain why you picked this answer.

1. After practicing yoga, Holly always felt _____.

   a. angry   b. relaxed   c. unhealthy   d. helpful

   _____

2. Joan read an ad in the newspaper that described just the kind of job she had always dreamed

   of having. Joan felt _____.

   a. excited   b. bored   c. goofy   d. unhappy

   _____

3. Roy had just lost his last dollar in the Coke machine. Roy was _____.

   a. angry   b. cool   c. shy   d. thrifty

   _____

4. When Charles learned he had just won fifty thousand dollars, tears ran down his cheeks. Charles was _____.

a. sad   b. confused   c. heartbroken   d. overcome with feeling

_____

5. John learned that his neighbor was having a party, and everybody else in the neighborhood had been invited. John felt _____.

a. reminded   b. remembered   c. refused   d. rejected

_____

6. Ted hated his boss, but he loved his job. When he was told that his boss was planning to move to Boston, he was _____.

a. scared   b. grouchy   c. thrilled   d. uncertain

_____

7. When the police phoned Mrs. Fox and told her that her son was safe, she felt _____.

a. understood   b. helpful   c. outspoken   d. thankful

_____

8. You have just completed the last lesson in the third reading book. You feel _____.

a. downhearted   b. joyful   c. wiped out   d. ready to start Book 4

_____

Review: Lessons 1–20

1 Word Study. Put the letter of the best answer on the line.

1. John *intended* to call his brother as soon as he got home from work. *Intend* means _____.

   a. to confront   b. to insist   c. to plan   d. to wonder

2. The actors always had *stage fright* just before the curtain went up. The actors _____.

   a. wanted people to enjoy their acting   c. forgot all their lines

   b. were edgy   d. needed help getting dressed for the play

3. By the time Dan got from the driveway to the porch, he was *drenched*. *Drenched* means _____.

   a. confused   b. exhausted   c. ready for dinner   d. soaked

4. Mr. Gray always felt *gloomy* just before and right after his birthday. *Gloomy* means _____.

   a. downhearted   b. excited   c. relaxed   d. tense

5. The Cowboys *trounced* the Colts in yesterday's football game. The Cowboys _____.

   a. barely won the game   c. lost the game

   b. beat the Colts badly   d. lost the game by quite a few touchdowns

6. The doctors believed they were on the *verge* of discovering a cure for cancer. The doctors _____.

   a. felt many more years of study would have to take place.

   b. felt they were about to make an important breakthrough.

   c. needed more money for the tests they were doing in their labs.

   d. thought things were hopeless.

7. Mr. Smith read *Consumer Reports* to learn more about which refrigerators were rated as the best buys. A *consumer* is someone who _____.

   a. buys goods

   b. cannot afford to spend more than he has to

   c. likes to own the best that money can buy

   d. needs advice about how he should spend his money

8. Paul *murmured* to his wife that he thought they should leave the party early. He _____.

    a. sent a note   c. spoke softly

    b. spoke loudly   d. stuttered

9. Ruth decided to take a few things out of her knapsack, so it would be easier to carry on the hike. The knapsack was probably too _____.

    a. bulky   b. costly   c. faulty   d. knotty

10. The speaker *concluded* his talk with a joke about people who fail to file their income tax returns. *Conclude* means _____.

    a. to begin   b. to break up   c. to end   d. to halt

11. When the manager informed the workers that they would not get their yearly raise, no one *uttered* a word. *Utter* means _____.

    a. to demand   b. to defend   c. to include   d. to speak

12. Cases of flu are *widespread* during the winter months. *Widespread* means _____.

    a. common   b. costly   c. disturbing   d. painful

13. Mr. Bloom was thought of as a *bigwig* by all the townspeople. He _____.

    a. was a very important person   c. worked for the town

    b. was known by most of the townspeople   d. was bald

14. Joan's first thought when she looked at the apartment was that it had a very *homey* look. Joan thought that the apartment was _____.

    a. cheap   b. fair   c. pleasant   d. well-done

15. When the teacher asked the class who invented the lightbulb, Jill *blurted* out the answer. She _____.

    a. gave the wrong answer

    b. guessed the answer and was right

    c. refused to give the answer

    d. spoke before she was called upon to give the answer

2 Words That Mean the Same. Match the words below with the word that means the same.

content	fussy	hoist	limit	staff
fib	grab	hurry	poor	want

_____ **1.** control

_____ **2.** desire

_____ **3.** grouchy

_____ **4.** lie

_____ **5.** needy

_____ **6.** pleased

_____ **7.** raise

_____ **8.** rush

_____ **9.** snatch

_____ **10.** workers

3 Word Opposites. Match the words below with the word that means the opposite.

costly	happiness	lying	shrink	straight
fancy	loosen	quiet	spotless	underneath

_____ **1.** crooked

_____ **2.** dirty

_____ **3.** expand

_____ **4.** noisy

_____ **5.** overhead

_____ **6.** plain

_____ **7.** sadness

_____ **8.** tighten

_____ **9.** truthful

_____ **10.** worthless

4 Syllables. Say each word out loud. On the lines to the right of each word, write the syllables you hear.

1. cloudless _____ • _____
2. successful _____ • _____ • _____
3. robber _____ • _____
4. sideways _____ • _____
5. thirteen _____ • _____

6. thoughtful _____ • _____
7. retire _____ • _____
8. handshake _____ • _____
9. protein _____ • _____
10. peacefully _____ • _____ • _____

5 Word Sounds. Choose the word in each line that has a different underlined sound. Write this word on the line to the right. Study the examples before you begin.

1. bl<u>a</u>de   r<u>a</u>nge   w<u>a</u>ke   w<u>a</u>lk   _____walk_____
2. <u>c</u>atch   <u>c</u>ity   <u>c</u>ode   <u>c</u>ome   _____city_____
3. <u>g</u>ame   <u>g</u>entle   <u>g</u>irl   <u>g</u>oal   _____
4. b<u>ea</u>t   gr<u>ea</u>t   l<u>ea</u>st   m<u>ea</u>l   _____
5. b<u>oo</u>th   g<u>oo</u>d   g<u>oo</u>se   r<u>oo</u>f   _____
6. b<u>ow</u>l   <u>ow</u>n   pl<u>ow</u>   sn<u>ow</u>   _____
7. bl<u>ou</u>se   c<u>ou</u>ld   p<u>ou</u>nd   sh<u>ou</u>t   _____
8. <u>ai</u>m   cert<u>ai</u>n   m<u>ai</u>l   w<u>ai</u>st   _____

6 Spelling Check. The answers to the clues are listed at the left. As you can see, the letters are all mixed up. Spell the words the right way on the lines. HINT: When you are done, the first letter of each answer, reading down, spells the name of a dessert.

c m o o o r r t u

1. _____ This is where you can find a judge and jury.

a g h h i w y

2. _____ This is where you can find lots of automobiles being driven home, to work, etc.

a d E g l n n

3. _____ This is a country where many people speak English.

e e g g h l l s

4. _____ This is where you can find a baby chick before it has hatched.

c h l o o s

5. _____ This is where you can go to take a course if you want to learn about something.

g e e s y i t h

6. _____ If you can see well, than this is good.

b c k k o o o o

7. _____ This is where you look if you want to find a new recipe to try out on your family or friends.

a a h r s t y

8. _____ This is where you put your ashes if you smoke.

c e h i k n t

9. _____ This is where you use the answer to Question 7. (It's a room in your house.)

t h a x u s e

10. _____ Sometimes you can see this coming out of a car or truck.

What is the name of the dessert that the first letters of each answer, reading down, spell?

_____

Word Index: Lessons 1–20

A

actor
admit
adult
advice
affair
afford
afraid
afterward
agree
ahead
ahoy
aim
alarm
aloud
already
although
anymore
anyone
apart
apartment
ape
appear
April Fool's
  Day
area
armful
arrest
arrive
aside
August
auto
automobile
autumn
avoid

B

backbone
backfire
background
backpack
bait
balance
balcony
barber
barge
bathing
bathtub
bead
beard
beast
beaten
beautiful
bedding
bedspread
bedtime
beg
beginning
behave

believe
bench
berserk
besides
bin
binge
birch
bitten
blackboard
blackmail
blacksmith
blade
blank
blast
blend
blessing
blindly
blond
bloody
bloom
blowout
blues
blurt
boardwalk
boast
boiler
bookcase
bookmark
bookshelf
bookstore
bookworm
boom
booth
border
borrow
bother
bottom
bound
bowl
bowling
brace
bracelet
brag
braid
brainy
branch
breakdown
breakthrough
breast
breed
breeze
bribe
brighter
broil
broken
brook
brownie
bruise
brush

bucket
building
bulk
bulky
Butch
buzz

C

café
camper
camping
cannot
cardboard
carpenter
carpet
caution
cautious
CD
certainly
chalk
chalkboard
charming
cheapskate
cheat
cheer
cheerful
cheerleader
cheery
chestnut
chick
chilly
chin
chirp
chore
chose
chow
chunk
cider
cinch
cinder
Cinderella
circle
circus
clam
clammy
clash
clearing
clearly
clench
clerk
cling
clingy
clothesline
clothespin
clothing
clumsy
clung
clutch
clutter
cob

cobweb
cockroach
cocoa
coconut
coffeecake
coldly
colt
combination
combine
comeback
comfort
coming
command
commander
commandment
comment
commit
commonly
compare
compete
complain
complaint
complete
completely
comply
compose
composed
composer
compute
conceal
concern
concert
conclude
confess
confide
confine
conform
confront
confuse
confusing
consent
consonant
construct
consume
consumer
contain
container
content
continue
contract
control
convince
cord
cork
corner
corpse
correct
costly
cough

counter
countless
courthouse
courtroom
cove
covering
cramp
crate
crick
cringe
crosswalk
crow
crowbar
crude
cruise
cruiser
crutch
crybaby
Cuban
cuff
cupboard
cure
cutting

D

daily
daring
Darkpill
darn
daughter
daybreak
daydream
deadline
debate
decay
December
declare
deepen
defeat
defend
define
delete
delight
demand
Dennis
dense
dentist
deny
depend
desire
despair
despite
dessert
destroy
detach
Detroit
devote
diet
difference
different

dill
dipstick
disagree
discharge
discover
discovery
discuss
disgust
dishpan
dishrag
dishwasher
display
dispose
disturb
diver
doggy
dome
doorbell
doorknob
doorman
doormat
dose
doubt
dough
doughnut
downcast
downfall
downhearted
downpour
downright
downstream
down-to-earth
drape
drawn
dread
dreadful
dreamer
dreamland
dreary
drench
dresser
dressing
drift
drill
drip
driven
driveway
drug
drugstore
dryer
dunce

E

earring
ease
eaten
e-card
edge
edgy
eighth

elbow
elf
elk
e-mail
enjoy
enter
etc.
eve
exact
exactly
exceed
except
exchange
excite
exclaim
excuse
exercise
exert
exhaust
exist
expand
expect
expel
expense
explode
explore
explorer
expose
express
extend
extent
extra
extreme
extremely
eyesight
eyestrain

F

fairly
fairness
fairy
faith
faithful
fallen
family
fancy
farmhouse
farther
fate
faucet
fault
faulty
favorite
feast
feather
figure
filter
finger
fingernail
fingerprint

fir
firelight
fireplace
fisherman
fitting
flail
flap
flashlight
flea
flight
flighty
flirt
floorboard
flowerpot
flu
fluff
flushed
flute
folk(s)
footing
footprint
forbid
force
forge
forgive
forgiven
forgotten
forth
freeway
freight
freshly
fright
frighten
frog
frown
frozen
fur
further

gag
Gail
gain
gale
gall
garbage
garlic
gauze
gaze
gear
gee
geese
gem
gentle
gentleman
gently
giggle
given
glance
glee
globe
gloom

gloomy
glove
glumly
gnarled
gnash
gnat
gnaw
gnawing
gnome
gob
gobble
godmother
golf
goodies
goof
goofy
gorge
gosh
grab
Grace
grace
grandfather
grandmother
grapevine
grasp
grease
greedy
greet
grief
gross
grouchy
growl
grudge
grumpy
grungy
gulf
gull
gully
gumdrop
gust
gut
gutter

H

habit
hail
hairbrush
hairpin
hairy
Halloween
halt
handshake
happiness
harass
hardware
harp
harsh
hasn't
hatch
haul
haunt
haunted

headache
heal
health food
heartbeat
heartbreak
heartbroken
height
hem
Herb
herb
highway
hip-hop
hoist
holder
holiday
Holly
homebody
homeland
homemade
homesick
homey
honor
horseback
horseplay
hotel
hourglass
hourly
housework
how's
huh
hurl
hurry
hush

I

icing
illness
import
imported
impose
impress
improper
improperly
improve
impure
include
income
increase
indoors
indulge
infect
inform
inhale
injure
injury
inquire
insect
insight
insist
inspire
instruct
intend

intent
invade
invent
invite
involve
iron
it'll
ivy

J

jelly
Jerome
jet
Joyce
joyful
judge
juice
juicy
jumpy
jury

K

keyboard
kidding
kin
kinfolk(s)
Kirk
kitchen
knack
knapsack
knee-deep
knelt
knight
knob
knockout
knotting
knotty

L

lampshade
lance
landlady
landlord
landmark
landowner
lard
lately
latest
laughter
laundromat
laundry
lawyer
lazy
leaky
leap
leapfrog
leash
leather
ledge
Lee
leftover
lemon

lesson
lifeguard
lightbulb
lighten
lighter
lighthouse
limit
lining
listen
lively
lodge
loose
loosen
lousy
lower
low-fat
loyally
loyalty
Luke
lukewarm
lunge
lurch
lying

M

machine
madly
mailbox
mailman
malt
manager
mankind
Mansfield
Martin
mash
matchbook
matchmaker
Matthew
mealtime
merge
message
midnight
mighty
Miguel
milkshake
mince
mincemeat
miscount
misjudge
misplace
misspell
mist
mistaken
mistreat
mistrust
moan
moist
moisten
mold
moldy
moment
moose

mope
motel
movement
murder
murmur
muscle
music

N

nasty
naughty
nearby
neatly
neighbor
neighborhood
neither
nervous
newspaper
newsstand
New Year's
   Day
New Year's
   Eve
nook
nor
notch
notice
November
nudge

O

oak
oat
oatmeal
October
oddly
ooze
ought
ours
ourselves
outcome
outdoors
outlook
outnumber
outskirts
outsmart
outspoken
outstanding
overboard
overcoat
overcome
overdone
overflow
overgrown
overhead
overnight
overseas
overtime
overweight
owe
ox

P

pact
padding
painful
painless
paintbrush
paperback
parent
passport
password
paste
patty
Paul
pause
pave
paving
peacefully
peanut
perch
perform
perk
piano
pigpen
pillow
pillowcase
pinch
pitch
pitcher
pitchfork
plainly
player
playground
plea
plead
pleasant
pleased
pledge
plenty
plow
plump
plunge
poach
poorhouse
poorly
porch
pose
pounce
pout
practice
praise
prance
prank
press
pretty
prince
probably
promise
prop
proper
properly
property

protein
pry
publisher
puffy
putty

Q

quarrel
quarter
quiet

R

racecourse
raft
rag
railroad
rainy
rarely
rash
ray
rear
recall
recipe
recover
reform
refresh
reject
rejection
rejoice
remark
repair
repeat
reply
reporter
require
respect
respond
restless
retire
retreat
reveal
review
ridden
ridge
ringside
rinse
risky
roadwork
roller
Rome
roof
rotten
rough
route
rowboat
royally
royalty
rut
Ruth

S

sadness

salsa
salty
Sam
sandwich
saucepan
saucer
savings
scald
scale
scarecrow
scary
scheme
scold
scoop
scorch
scoreboard
Scotch
Scott
scour
scram
scraper
scratchy
screw
script
scroll
scrounge
scruff
seacoast
seafood
seaport
season
seaweed
serving
shade
shady
shaken
shark
she'd
sheer
shelf
shelter
she's
shipwreck
shootout
shopper
shopping
shortcake
shorts
shoulder
shove
shown
shy
shyly
sideshow
sidewalk
sift
silk
silky
sill
single
sir

skater
sketch
ski
skid
skillful
skinless
skinny
skip
skull
slacks
slaughter
sled
sleepover
sleet
sleigh
slept
slid
slide
slight
slipper
slot
slouch
slowdown
slowpoke
slump
smack
smear
Smith
smog
smoky
smooth
smoothly
smudge
snapshot
snarl
snatch
sneak
sneakers
sneaky
sneer
sniff
snowball
snowplow
snowstorm
snowy
soar
softly
sole
son
sooner
sought
source
sourpuss
spaceship
spaghetti
span
spark
special
speck
sped
speech

spendthrift
spied
spine
spit
splurge
spoken
spoonful
spy
square
squarely
squirm
staff
stairway
standstill
starch
starfish
stash
station
steel
stem
Steve
Steven
stew
stir
stitch
stocking
stony
stool
stoop
stork
straighten
stray
streak
stress
stressful
stretch
stretchy
stuffing
stuffy
stumble
stunt
stutter
subject
successfully
suit
suitcase
sulk
sulky
sundown
sunken
sunless
sunrise
suppose
swam
Swede
Sweden
sweep
sweeper
swept
Swiss
syllable

system

T

tablecloth
tag
tailspin
tasteless
tasty
taught
Ted
tee
teepee
tennis
tense
Thanksgiving
theft
themselves
they're
thickly
thief
thinner
thirst
thirsty
thorn
thread
threaten
thrift
thrifty
thrill
throat
throughout
thud
thump
tighten
tightly
till
tilt
together
toil
Tony
toolbox
toothbrush
toothpaste
tough
tow
townspeople
tow truck
trace
trainer
trance
tread
trend
trespass
tribe
tricky
troll
troop
trooper
trounce
trousers
trout
truce

trudge
truthfully

U

unafraid
uncertain
unclear
uncooked
uncover
underdog
underground
underneath
undershirt
understand
understated
understood
undertaker
underwear
undid
undo
uneasy
uneven
unfit
unhealthy
unit
universe
unlawful
unlikely
unpack
unpaid
untrained
unwilling
upbeat
upcoming
update
upkeep
uproar
upscale
upside-down
upstairs
uptown
urge

V

Valentine's Day
vane
vanilla
veal
verge
video
vine
visit
voice mail
void
volt
vow

W

waist
waistline
waiter
waitress

wallet
Walter
waltz
wander
warmer
warmly
washcloth
washing
wastebasket
watchman
weaken
weather
website
wedding
weeknight
weight
we'll
well done
weren't
whack
wham
whatsoever
wheeze
whether
whichever
whim
whine
whoever
who's
widespread
wildflower
wildly
William
wilt
window
wise
wisecrack
wisely
woods
workout
workshop
wrapper
wrapping
wrecker
wren
wrench
wring
wrung

X

Y

yeah
yearly
YMCA
yoga
you'd
you'll
you've
yuck

Z

Word Index: Books 1-3

A

a
able
about
above
according
ace
across
act
action
actor
ad
add
address
admit
adult
advice
affair
afford
afraid
after
afternoon
afterward
again
against
age
ago
agree
ahead
ahoy
aid
ail
aim
air
alarm
Alaskan
alive
all
allow
all right
almost
alone
along
aloud
alphabet
already
also
although
always
am
America
amuse
amusement

an
and
Andy
anger
angry
animal
Ann(e)
another
answer
ant
any
anybody
anymore
anyone
anything
anyway
anywhere
apart
apartment
ape
appear
April
April Fool's
  Day
are
area
aren't
arm
armchair
armful
army
around
arrest
arrive
art
as
ash
ashtray
aside
ask
asleep
at
ate
auction
August
aunt
auto
automobile
autumn
avoid
awake
awareness
away
awful

awoke

B

baby
babysit
babysitter
back
backbone
backfire
background
backpack
bad
badge
badly
bag
bail
bait
bake
baker
balance
balcony
bald
ball
ban
band
bang
bank
banker
bar
barbed
barbed wire
barber
bare
barely
barge
bark
barn
Bart
base
baseball
basket
basketball
bat
batch
bath
bathe
bathing
bathroom
bathtub
batter
battle
BC
be
beach

bead
bean
bear
beard
beast
beat
beaten
beautiful
became
because
Becky
become
bed
bedding
bedroom
bedspread
bedtime
bee
beef
beekeeper
been
beep
beer
beeswax
beet
before
beg
began
begin
beginning
begun
behave
behind
believe
bell
below
belt
beluga
Ben
bench
bend
bent
berry
berserk
beside
besides
best
bet
better
between
bib
Bible
bid
big

bigwig
bike
bill
billion
Billy
bin
bind
binge
birch
bird
birth
birthday
bit
bite
bitten
bitter
black
blackbird
blackboard
blackmail
blacksmith
blade
blame
blank
blast
bleach
bleed
blend
bless
blessing
blew
blind
blindly
blink
blob
block
blond
blood
bloodstream
bloody
bloom
blouse
blow
blown
blowout
blue
blueberry
blues
bluff
blurt
blush
board
boarder
boardwalk

boast
boat
Bob
body
bodyguard
boil
boiler
bold
bolt
bomb
bond
bone
bony
book
bookcase
bookmark
bookshelf
bookstore
bookworm
boom
boot
booth
border
bore
born
borrow
boss
Boston
both
bother
bottom
bought
bounce
bouncy
bound
bow
bowl
bowling
box
boxer
boy
boyfriend
brace
bracelet
brag
braid
brain
brainy
brake
branch
brand
brand-new
brave
bravely

bread
break
breakdown
breakfast
breakthrough
breast
breath
breathe
breathing
breathless
breed
breeze
bribe
brick
bride
bridge
bright
brighter
bring
brink
broil
broke
broken
brook
brother
brought
brown
brownie
bruise
brush
buck
bucket
bud
buddy
bug
build
building
built
bulb
bulk
bulky
bull
bum
bump
bumper
bumpy
bun
bunch
bunk
bunt
burn
burp
burst
bus

bus stop
bush
business
bust
busy
busybody
but
Butch
butter
buy
buzz
by

C

cab
café
cage
cake
calf
California
call
calm
calmly
came
camp
camper
camping
can
Canada
Canadian
cancer
candy
candy bar
candy cane
cane
cannot
can't
cap
cape
Cape Cod
car
card
cardboard
care
careful
careless
carpenter
carpet
carry
cart
carve
case
cash
casino
cast
cat

catbird
catch
catcher
catfish
cattlemen
caught
cause
caution
cautious
cave
CD
ceiling
celebrate
celebration
cell
cellar
cell phone
cent
center
cereal
certain
certainly
chain
chair
chalk
chalkboard
chance
change
charge
Charles
charm
charming
chart
chase
cheap
cheaply
cheapskate
cheat
check
checkbook
cheek
cheer
cheerful
cheerleader
cheery
cheese
cheesecake
chemical
chess
chessboard
chest
chestnut
chew
chick
chicken
child

children
chill
chilly
chin
chirp
chocolate
choice
choke
choose
chop
chore
chose
chow
Christ
Christmas
chrome
chronic
chunk
church
cider
cigar
cigarette
cinch
cinder
Cinderella
circle
circus
city
claim
clam
clammy
clap
clash
class
classroom
claw
clay
clean
cleaner
clear
clearing
clearly
clench
clerk
click
climb
cling
clingy
clip
clock
close
cloth
clothes
clothesline
clothespin
clothing

cloud
cloudless
cloudy
clown
club
clue
clumsy
clung
clutch
clutter
coach
coal
coast
coat
cob
cobweb
cockroach
cocoa
coconut
cod
code
coffee
coffeecake
coil
coin
Coke
cold
coldly
colony
colt
comb
combination
combine
come
comeback
comfort
coming
command
commander
commandment
comment
commit
common
commonly
compare
compete
complain
complaint
complete
completely
complex
comply
compose
composed
composer
compound

compute
computer
conceal
concern
concert
conclude
cone
confess
confide
confine
conform
confront
confuse
confusing
consent
consonant
construct
consume
consumer
contain
container
content
continue
contract
control
convict
convince
cook
cookbook
cool
cop
cope
copper
copy
cord
cork
corn
corner
cornflakes
corpse
correct
cost
costly
cot
couch
cough
could
couldn't
count
counter
countless
country
countrymen
course
court
courthouse

courtroom
cousin
cove
cover
covering
cow
cowboy
crack
cracker
cramp
craps
crash
crate
crawl
crazy
creak
cream
creep
creepy
crib
crick
crime
cringe
crook
crooked
crop
cross
crosswalk
crouch
crow
crowbar
crowd
crown
crude
cruise
cruiser
crumb
crunch
crust
crutch
cry
crybaby
cub
Cuban
cube
cuff
cup
cupboard
cupcake
curb
cure
curl
curse
curtain
curve
cut

cute
cutters
cutting

D

dab
dad
daily
dam
damp
Dan
dance
dancer
danger
Danny
dare
daring
dark
Darkpill
darn
dart
dash
date
daughter
Dave
dawn
day
daybreak
daydream
daylight
dead
deadline
deadly
deal
dear
death
debate
decay
December
decide
deck
declare
deed
deep
deepen
deer
defeat
defend
define
delete
delight
demand
den
Dennis
dense
dent

dentist	does	drink	eighteen	explore	fed	flea
deny	doesn't	drip	eighth	explorer	fee	flesh
depend	dog	drive	eighty	expose	feed	flew
describe	doggy	driven	either	express	feel	flight
deserve	dollar	driver	elbow	extend	feeling	flighty
desire	dome	driveway	El Dorado	extent	feet	flip
desk	done	drop	eleven	extra	fell	flirt
despair	donkey	drove	elf	extreme	felt	float
despite	Donna	drug	elk	extremely	female	flock
dessert	don't	drugstore	elm	eye	fence	flood
destroy	door	drum	else	eyesight	fetch	floor
detach	doorbell	drunk	Elvis	eyestrain	few	floorboard
Detroit	doorknob	dry	e-mail		fib	flop
devote	doorman	dryer	employer	**F**	fiddle	flour
dice	doormat	duck	empty		fiddler	flow
Dick	doorway	due	end	face	field	flower
did	dope	dues	endangered	fact	fifteen	flowerpot
diddle	dose	dug	ending	factor	fifty	flu
didn't	dot	duke	energy	factory	fig	fluff
die	double	dull	England	fad	fight	flush
diet	doubt	dumb	English	fade	fighter	flushed
difference	dough	dump	enjoy	fail	figure	flute
different	doughnut	dunce	enough	faint	file	fly
dig	down	dune	enter	fair	fill	fog
dill	downcast	dunk	environment	fairly	filter	foggy
dim	downfall	during	etc.	fairness	fin	fold
dime	downhearted	dusk	Europe	fairy	find	folder
dine	downhill	dust	eve	faith	fine	folk(s)
diner	downpour	dusty	even	faithful	finger	fond
dining room	downright	Dutch	evening	fake	fingernail	food
dinner	downstairs	dwarf	ever	fall	fingerprint	fool
dip	downstream		every	fallen	fir	foot
dipstick	down-to-earth	**E**	everybody	false	fire	football
dirt	downtown		everyone	fame	firecracker	footing
dirty	doze	each	everything	family	firelight	footprint
disagree	dozen	ear	everywhere	fan	fireplace	for
discharge	Dr.	early	exact	fancy	firm	forbid
discover	drag	earn	exactly	fang	firmly	force
discovery	drain	earring	example	far	first	fore
discuss	drank	earth	exceed	fare	fish	forefeet
disease	drape	ease	except	farm	fisherman	forest
disgust	draw	easily	exchange	farmer	fist	forge
dish	drawn	east	excite	farmhouse	fit	forget
dishpan	dread	easy	exclaim	farther	fitting	forgetful
dishrag	dreadful	eat	excuse	fast	five	forgive
dishwasher	dream	eaten	exercise	fat	fix	forgiven
display	dreamer	e-card	exert	fate	flag	forgot
dispose	dreamland	Eddie	exhaust	father	flail	forgotten
disturb	dreary	edge	exist	faucet	flake	fork
ditch	drench	edgy	expand	fault	flaky	form
dive	dress	eel	expect	faulty	flame	forth
diver	dresser	effect	expel	favorite	flap	fortune
do	dressing	effort	expense	fear	flare	fortune-teller
dock	drew	egg	expert	fearful	flash	forty
doctor	drift	eggshell	explain	feast	flashlight	forty-niner
dodge	drill	Egypt	explode	feather	flat	forward
		eight		February		

fought
found
four
fourteen
fourth
Fourth of July
fox
frame
France
free
freedom
freeway
freeze
freezer
freight
French
French fries
fresh
freshly
Friday
friend
friendly
fright
frighten
frog
from
front
frown
froze
frozen
fruit
fruitcake
fry
fudge
full
fume
fun
fund(s)
funk
funny
fur
further
fuse
fuss
fussily
fussy
future

G

gag
Gail
gain
gale
gall
galley
gallon

game
gang
garbage
garlic
gas
gate
gauze
gave
Gaylord
gaze
gear
gee
geese
gem
gentle
gentleman
gently
George
germ
get
gift
giggle
gill
gin
ginger
gingerbread
girl
girlfriend
give
given
glad
glance
gland
glare
glass
gleam
glee
glitter
globe
gloom
gloomy
glove
glue
glumly
gnarled
gnash
gnat
gnaw
gnawing
gnome
go
goal
gob
gobble
God
godmother

goes
gold
gold-plated
golf
gone
gong
good
goodies
goodness
goof
goofy
goose
gorge
gosh
got
gotten
gown
grab
Grace
grace
grade
grain
grand
grandfather
grandmother
grandstand
grape
grapefruit
grapevine
grasp
grass
grave
graveyard
gray
grease
great
greed
greedy
green
greet
grew
grief
grill
grin
grip
gripe
groan
groom
gross
grouch
grouchy
ground
group
grow
growl

grown
grown-up
grudge
grumpy
grungy
guard
guess
guest
guide
guilt
guilty
gulf
gull
gully
gum
gumdrop
gun
gust
gut
gutter
guy

H

habit
had
hadn't
hail
hair
hairbrush
haircut
hairless
hairpin
hairy
half
hall
Halloween
halt
ham
hammer
hand
handful
handle
handshake
handwriting
handy
hang
hanger
happen
happily
happiness
happy
harass
hard
hardly
hardware
harm

harmful
harmless
harp
harsh
has
hasn't
hat
hatch
hate
haul
haunt
haunted
have
haven't
hay
he
head
headache
heading
heal
health
health food
healthy
hear
heard
heart
heartbeat
heartbreak
heartbroken
heat
heater
heavily
heavy
heck
he'd
heel
height
held
helicopter
hell
hello
helmet
help
helper
helpful
helpless
hem
hen
her
Herb
herb
herd
here
herself
he's
hey

hi
hid
hidden
hide
high
high-class
high school
highway
hike
hill
him
himself
hint
hip
hip-hop
hire
his
hit
hive
hobby
hock
hoist
hold
holder
holdup
hole
holiday
Holly
home
homebody
homeland
homeless
homemade
homesick
homework
homey
honey
honeybee
honk
honor
hood
hook
hop
hope
hopeful
hopeless
horn
horse
horseback
horseplay
hose
host
hot
hotel
hour
hourglass

hourly
house
household
housework
how
however
how's
hug
huge
huh
hum
human
hunch
hundred
hung
hunt
hunter
hurl
hurry
hurt
hush
hut

I

I
ice
ice cream
icing
icy
I'd
idea
if
ill
I'll
illness
I'm
import
important
imported
impose
impress
improper
improperly
improve
impure
in
include
income
increase
indoors
indulge
infect
inform
inhale
injure
injury

ink
inland
inquire
insect
inside
insight
insist
inspire
instead
instruct
intend
intent
Internet
into
invade
invent
invite
involve
iron
is
isn't
issue
it
itch
it's
its
I've
ivy

J

jab
Jack
jacket
jail
jam
January
Japan
jar
jaw
jazz
jeans
jeep
jeer
jelly
jerk
Jerome
jet
Jill
Jim
Joan
job
jobless
John
join
joint
joke

joker
Jones
jot
journal
joy
Joyce
joyful
judge
jug
juice
juicy
July
jump
jumpy
June
junk
jury
just

K

Kate
keel
keep
keeper
kept
ketchup
key
keyboard
kick
kid
kidding
kidnap
kill
kin
kind
kinfolk(s)
king
King Solomon
Kirk
kiss
kit
kitchen
kite
kitty
knack
knapsack
knee
kneecap
knee-deep
kneel
knelt
knew
knife
knight
knit
knitter

knob
knock
knockout
knot
knotting
knotty
know
known

L

lab
lace
lack
lady
laid
lake
lamb
lame
lamp
lampshade
lance
land
landlady
landlord
landmark
landowner
lane
lap
lapdog
laptop
lard
large
lark
Las Vegas
last
late
lately
later
latest
laugh
laughter
laundromat
laundry
law
lawful
lawn
lawyer
lay
lazy
lead
leaf
leak
leaky
lean
leap
leapfrog

learn
leash
least
leather
leave
led
ledge
Lee
left
leftover
leg
lemon
lend
lent
less
lesson
let
let's
letter
lice
lick
lid
lie
life
lifeboat
lifeguard
lifetime
lift
light
lightbulb
lighten
lighter
lighthouse
like
limb
lime
limit
limp
line
lining
link
lint
lip
lipstick
liquid
list
listen
lit
little
live
lively
load
loaf
lobby
lock
lodge

log
lone
lonely
long
look
loose
loosen
lord
lose
lost
lot
loud
loudly
Louise
lousy
love
loveliest
lovely
lover
low
lower
low-fat
loyal
loyally
loyalty
luck
luckily
lucky
lug
Luke
lukewarm
lump
lunch
lung
lunge
lurch
lying

M

machine
Mack
mad
made
madly
maid
mail
mailbox
mailman
main
mainly
make
maker
male
mall
malt
mammal

man
manager
mankind
Mansfield
many
map
march
March
Mark
mark
marry
Martin
Mary
mash
mask
mass
mat
match
matchbook
matchmaker
mate
math
matter
Matthew
May
may
maybe
me
meal
mealtime
mean
meaning
meaningful
meant
meat
meatball
meatless
medical
meet
meeting
melt
men
mend
mention
meow
merge
mess
message
messy
met
mice
microwave
middle
middle-aged
midnight
might

mighty
Miguel
Mike
mild
mile
milk
milkshake
million
mince
mincemeat
mind
mine
miner
Min-hee
mint
minute
mirror
miscount
misjudge
misplace
miss
misspell
mist
mistake
mistaken
mistreat
mistrust
mitt
mix
moan
mob
mock
moist
moisten
mold
moldy
mole
mom
moment
Monday
money
monkey
month
mood
moon
moose
mop
mope
more
morning
most
motel
mother
mouse
mouth
mouthful

move
movement
movie
mow
mower
Mr.
Mrs.
Ms.
much
mud
muddy
mug
muggy
mule
munch
murder
murmur
muscle
muse
music
must
mute
my
myself

N

nail
name
nap
nasty
native
natural
naughty
near
nearby
nearly
neat
neatly
neck
necktie
need
needless
needy
neighbor
neighborhood
neither
Nelson
nerve
nervous
nest
net
never
new
news
newspaper
newsstand

New Year's
 Day
New Year's
 Eve
New York
next
nice
nick
nickname
night
nine
nineteen
ninety
nip
no
nobody
nod
noise
noisily
noisy
none
nook
noon
no one
nope
nor
north
nose
nosy
not
notch
note
notebook
nothing
notice
November
now
nowhere
nude
nudge
numb
number
nurse
nut
nutty

O

oak
oar
oat
oatmeal
ocean
o'clock
October
odd
oddly

of
off
often
oh
oil
okay
old
on
once
one
online
only
ooze
open
opposite
or
order
other
ouch
ought
ounce
our
ours
ourselves
out
outcome
outdoors
outlook
outnumber
outside
outskirts
outsmart
outspoken
outstanding
oven
over
overboard
overcoat
overcome
overdone
overflow
overgrown
overhead
overnight
overseas
overtime
overweight
owe
own
owner
ox

P

pace
pack
pact

pad
padding
page
paid
pail
pain
painful
painless
paint
paintbrush
painter
painting
pair
pale
palm
pan
pancake
pant
pants
paper
paperback
parent
park
part
party
pass
passport
password
past
paste
pat
patch
path
patty
Paul
pause
pave
paving
paw
pawn
pay
paycheck
payday
payment
pea
peace
peaceful
peacefully
peach
peanut
pear
peck
peek
peel
peer
pen

penny
people
pep
pepper
peppermint
pepperoni
percent
perch
perform
period
perk
person
pest
pet
phone
piano
pick
picture
pie
piece
pig
piggy
pigpen
pile
pill
pillow
pillowcase
pin
pinch
pine
pink
Pinocchio
pint
pipe
pit
pitch
pitcher
pitchfork
pity
pizza
place
plain
plainly
plan
plane
planet
plant
plate
play
player
playground
plea
plead
pleasant
please
pleased

pledge
plenty
plot
plow
plug
plum
plump
plunge
plus
poach
pod
poem
poet
point
pointless
poke
pole
police
policeman
policewoman
pollen
pollution
pond
pool
poor
poorhouse
poorly
pop
popcorn
porch
pork
pork chop
port
pose
post
pot
potato
pouch
pounce
pound
pour
pout
power
practice
praise
prance
prank
pray
present
president
press
pretty
price
pride
prince
print

prize
probably
problem
product
promise
proof
prop
proper
properly
property
protect
protein
proud
prune
pry
public
publisher
puff
puffy
pull
pulse
pump
punch
punt
purr
purse
push
put
putty

Q

quack
quarrel
quart
quarter
queen
question
quick
quickly
quiet
quit
quite

R

race
racecourse
rack
raft
rag
rage
raid
rail
railroad
rain
rainbow
raincoat

rainy
raise
rake
ram
ramp
ran
rang
range
rank
rare
rarely
rash
rat
rate
raw
ray
reach
react
read
reading
ready
real
really
rear
reason
recall
recipe
record
recover
recycle
red
reduce
reel
refill
reform
refresh
refrigerator
refund
refuse
reject
rejection
rejoice
relate
relax
remain
remark
remember
remind
remove
renew
rent
repair
repay
repeat
reply
report

reporter
require
resource
respect
respond
rest
restaurant
restless
restroom
retire
retreat
return
reveal
review
rhyme
rib
rice
rich
rid
ridden
ride
ridge
rig
right
ring
ringside
rinse
rip
ripe
rise
risk
risky
river
road
roadwork
roar
roast
roast beef
rob
robber
robbery
robe
rock
rod
rode
role
roll
roller
Rome
roof
room
rope
rose
rosy
rot
rotten

rough
round
route
row
rowboat
Roy
royal
royally
royalty
rub
rude
rug
rule
ruler
run
rung
runny
runt
rush
rust
rut
Ruth

S

sack
sad
sadly
sadness
safe
safely
said
sail
sale
salsa
salt
salty
Sam
same
sand
sandwich
sandy
sang
sank
sat
Saturday
sauce
saucepan
saucer
saucy
save
savings
saw
say
saying
says
scald

scale
scar
scare
scarecrow
scared
scary
scheme
school
school bus
scold
scoop
scooter
scorch
score
scoreboard
Scotch
Scott
scour
scout
scram
scramble
scrap
scrape
scraper
scratch
scratchy
scream
screech
screen
screw
scribe
script
scroll
scrounge
scrub
scruff
sea
seacoast
seafood
seaport
search
seasick
season
seat
seaweed
second
see
seed
seek
seem
seen
seep
self
sell
senator
send

sense
sent
sentence
September
serve
serving
set
seven
seventeen
seventh
seventy
Seven Up
shack
shade
shady
shake
shaken
shaky
shame
shape
share
shark
sharp
sharply
shatter
shave
she
she'd
sheep
sheer
sheet
shelf
shell
shelter
she's
shift
shine
shiny
ship
shipwreck
shirt
shock
shook
shoot
shootout
shop
shopper
shopping
shore
short
shortcake
shorts
shortstop
shot
shotgun
should

shoulder
shouldn't
shout
shove
show
shower
shown
shrank
shred
shrill
shrimp
shrink
shrug
shrunk
shut
shy
shyly
sick
side
sideshow
sidewalk
sideways
sift
sigh
sight
sign
silent
silk
silky
sill
silly
simple
simply
sin
since
sing
singer
single
sink
sip
sir
sister
sit
sitter
six
sixteen
sixty
skate
skater
sketch
ski
skid
skill
skillful
skin
skinless

skinny
skip
skirt
skull
skunk
sky
slack
slacks
slam
slang
slant
slap
slaughter
sled
sleep
sleepily
sleepless
sleepover
sleepy
sleet
sleeve
sleeveless
sleigh
slept
slice
slid
slide
slight
slim
sling
slip
slipper
slot
slouch
slow
slowdown
slowly
slowpoke
slump
slung
slush
smack
small
smart
smash
smear
smell
smile
Smith
smog
smoke
smoker
smoky
smooth
smoothly
smudge

snack
snag
snail
snake
snap
snappy
snapshot
snarl
snatch
sneak
sneakers
sneaky
sneer
sneeze
sniff
snob
snore
snow
Snow White
snowball
snowplow
snowstorm
snowy
so
soak
soap
soar
sob
sock
socks
soft
softly
soil
sold
sole
solid
some
somebody
someday
someone
something
sometimes
son
song
soon
sooner
sore
sorry
sort
sought
sound
soundly
soup
sour
source
sourpuss
south

space
spaceship
spaghetti
Spain
span
spank
spare
spare rib
spark
speak
speaker
special
species
speck
sped
speech
speed
spell
spend
spendthrift
spent
spice
spicy
spill
spin
spine
spit
spite
spiteful
splash
spleen
splint
splinter
split
splurge
spoil
spoke
spoken
spoon
spoonful
sport
spot
spotless
sprain
sprang
sprawl
spray
spread
spring
sprint
spy
square
squarely
squash
squat
squeal
squeeze

squid
squirm
squirrel
squirt
staff
stage
stagecoach
stain
stair
stairway
stale
stamp
stand
standstill
star
starch
stare
starfish
start
starve
stash
state
station
stay
steak
steam
steel
steep
steer
stem
step
Steve
Steven
stew
stick
sticker
sticky
still
sting
stinger
stink
stir
stitch
stocking
stomach
stone
stony
stood
stool
stoop
stop
store
stork
storm
story
stove
straight

straighten
strain
strand
strange
stranger
strap
straw
strawberry
stray
streak
stream
street
streetlight
stress
stressful
stretch
stretchy
strict
strike
string
strip
stripe
stroke
strong
struck
struggle
stuck
study
stuff
stuffing
stuffy
stumble
stunt
stutter
sub
subject
success
successful
successfully
such
suck
suddenly
suds
Sue
sue
sugar
sugarless
sugary
suit
suitcase
sulk
sulky
sum
summer
sun
sunburn
Sunday

sundown
sung
sunglasses
sunk
sunken
sunless
sunlight
sunny
sunrise
sunshine
suppose
sure
surely
surf
surfer
Surgeon
    General
surprise
Sutter
swam
swear
sweat
sweater
Swede
Sweden
sweep
sweeper
sweet
swell
swept
swerve
swift
swiftly
swim
swimmer
swing
swipe
Swiss
switch
swizzle
sworn
swung
syllable
system

T

tab
table
tablecloth
tablespoon
tack
tag
tail
tailor
tailspin
take

taken
tale
talk
tall
tame
tan
tank
tap
tape
tar
task
taste
tasteless
tasty
taught
tax
tea
teabag
teach
teacher
team
teamwork
tear
tease
teaspoon
Ted
tee
teepee
teeth
television
tell
teller
temper
temperature
temple
ten
tend
tennis
tense
tent
term
test
than
thank
thankful
Thanksgiving
that
that's
thaw
the
theft
their
them
themselves
then
there
there's

these
they
they're
thick
thickly
thief
thin
thing
think
thinker
thinner
third
thirst
thirsty
thirteen
thirty
this
thorn
those
though
thought
thoughtful
thoughtless
thousand
thread
threat
threaten
three
threw
thrift
thrifty
thrill
throat
throne
through
throughout
throw
thrown
thud
thumb
thump
Thursday
tick
ticket
tide
tie
tight
tighten
tightly
tile
till
tilt
Tim
time
timeless
tin
tiny

tip
tire
to
toast
toaster
tobacco
today
together
toil
told
Tom
tomato
tomorrow
ton
tone
tonight
Tony
too
took
tool
toolbox
tooth
toothbrush
toothpaste
top
tore
torn
toss
touch
touchdown
tough
tow
toward
towel
town
townspeople
tow truck
toy
trace
track
trade
trail
train
trainer
trance
trap
trapper
trash
tray
tread
treat
tree
trend
trespass
tribe
trick
tricky

trim
trip
troll
troop
trooper
trouble
troublemaker
trounce
trousers
trout
truce
truck
trudge
true
trunk
trust
truth
truthful
truthfully
try
tub
tube
tuck
Tuesday
tug
tune
turn
TV
twelve
twenty
twice
twin
twine
twist
two

U

ugly
unable
unafraid
unarmed
uncertain
unclear
uncooked
uncover
under
underdog
underground
underline
underneath
undershirt
understand
understated
understood
undertaker

underwear
undid
undo
undress
uneasy
uneven
unfair
unfit
unfold
unfriendly
unhappy
unhealthy
unit
United States
universe
unlawful
unless
unlikely
unlucky
unmade
unpack
unpaid
unprotected
unsafe
untie
until
untrained
unwilling
unwrap
up
up-and-down
upbeat
upcoming
update
uphill
upkeep
upon
uproar
upscale
upset
upside-down
upstairs
uptown
urge
us
use
useful
useless
utter

V

Valentine's
  Day
van
vane
vanilla

vase
veal
vegetable
verge
Vermont
verse
very
vest
vice
video
vine
visit
voice
voice mail
void
volt
vote
voter
vow
vowel

W

wade
wage
waist
waistline
wait
waiter
waitress
wake
walk
wall
wallet
Walter
waltz
wander
want
war
warm
warmer
warmly
warn
warning
was
wash
washcloth
washing
Washington
wasn't
waste
wastebasket
wasteful
watch
watchful
watchman
water

watery
wave
wavy
wax
way
we
weak
weaken
wear
weather
web
website
wed
wedding
Wednesday
weed
week
weekend
weekly
weeknight
weep
weigh
weight
well
we'll
well-done
well-known
went
were
we're
weren't
west
wet
whack
whale
wham
what
whatever
what's
whatsoever
wheat
wheel
wheeze
when
whenever
where
wherever
whether
which
whichever
while
whim
whine
whip
whirl
white
who

whoever
whole
whom
who's
whose
why
wide
widespread
wife
wig
wild
wildflower
wildly
will
William
wilt
win
wind
window
wine
wing
wink
winner
winter
wipe
wire
wiry
Wisconsin
wise
wisecrack
wisely
wish
witch
with
without
woke
wolf
woman
women
won
wonder
won't
wood
woods
wool
word
wore
work
worker
workout
workshop
world
worn
worry
worse
worst
worth

worthless
worthy
would
wouldn't
wound
wow
wrap
wrapper
wrapping
wreck
wrecker
wren
wrench
wring
wrist
write
writer
written
wrong
wrote
wrung

X

Y

yard
yawn
yeah
year
yearly
yell
yellow
yes
yesterday
yet
YMCA
yoga
yolk
you
you'd
you'll
young
your
you're
yourself
you've
yuck

Z

zip
zipper
zone
zoo

Answer Key

Lesson 1

1 About the Story

1. Steven drives a van for a living.
2. He has had this job for five years.
3. His sister's name is Ruth.
4. Steven sees Ruth once a week, on Thursday night.
5. a. The exercise class would help Steven feel more relaxed.
   b. The class would also give him an opportunity to meet new people.
6. At first, Steven gets angry.
7. At the end of the story, Steven decides to give the class a try.
8. A pact is an agreement or deal.
9. Answers may vary. Ruth may be encouraging Steven to "go out more, do things, and meet some new people" because she enjoys these activities. On the other hand, Steven does visit her every Thursday and she may be trying to prevent him from getting into a rut like she has.
10. Ruth tells Steven that he is still young, and he has been driving a van for five years. Therefore he is probably in his mid-twenties.

2 The Ending -ing

1. blessing	1. bathing	1. bedding
2. building	2. lining	2. knotting
3. clearing	3. paving	3. fitting
4. dressing	4. confusing	4. cutting
5. stuffing	5. coming	5. padding
6. washing	6. icing	6. wedding

3 How Do These People Earn a Living?

1. teacher	5. miner	8. dishwasher
2. baker	6. waiter	9. teller
3. farmer	7. coach	10. lawyer
4. driver		

4 Compound Words

1. road + work	5. back + fire	8. man + kind
2. side + walk	6. dish + pan	9. home + made
3. tool + box	7. pig + pen	10. news + paper
4. grape + vine		

Lesson 2

1 About the Story

1. Steven's best friend is Jerome.
2. Steven is taking a yoga class at the YMCA.
3. He wandered into the yoga class by mistake.
4. Jerome thinks yoga has stranger exercises.
5. Jerome didn't laugh at Steven for taking the yoga class.
6. Jerome seems to have let himself into Steven's apartment, and he helps himself to the stew Steven has made for dinner.

2 Adding -est to Words

1. finest	1. proudest	1. saddest
2. rudest	2. shortest	2. biggest
3. nicest	3. cheapest	3. thinnest
4. latest	4. greatest	4. dimmest
5. ripest	5. meanest	5. maddest
6. sorest	6. highest	6. hottest

3 How Do These People Earn a Living?

1. reporter	5. tailor	9. shortstop
2. carpenter	6. babysitter	10. fisherman
3. bodyguard	7. trainer	11. scribe
4. actor	8. clown	12. doctor

4 Compound Words

1. pay + check	5. chalk + board	9. flash + light
2. tooth + paste	6. short + cake	10. cook + book
3. under + stand	7. class + room	11. work + shop
4. lamp + shade	8. under + shirt	12. hand + shake

Lesson 3

1 About the Story

1. Jerome does an Internet search on the subject.
2. Jerome thinks Steven is clumsy.
3. He thinks Steven will break a limb and end up on crutches.
4. Jerome remembers that Steven stood on his head the other day and didn't lose his balance.
5. Jerome believes it must be easier than it looks.
6. No, because there are crumbs and dust on the floor, and his room is full of clutter.
7. To flail means to move in a clumsy way.
8. Jerome decides yoga is hard because he can't do it, and because there are so many books written about it.
9. Jerome learns more about yoga online and decides it can't be hard if his clumsy friend Steven can do it, but Jerome falls after trying to stand on his head and decides yoga must be hard after all.

2 Adding -y to Words

1. tasty	1. flighty	1. runny
2. shaky	2. stuffy	2. doggy
3. shady	3. clingy	3. patty
4. stony	4. rainy	4. knotty
5. edgy	5. leaky	5. clammy

3 Who Uses What?

1. oven	5. mower	9. computer
2. brain	6. map	10. words
3. tent	7. mitt	11. jokes
4. brakes	8. spell	12. proof

4 Compound Words

1. black + board
2. ear + ring
3. milk + shake
4. fruit + cake
5. over + grown
6. hair + brush
7. sun + light
8. suit + case
9. eye + strain
10. snow + ball
11. race + course
12. free + way

Lesson 4

1 About the Story

1. Ginger is trying to sleep.
2. It will help her sleep better and feel less stressed out. It is good for the mind and body. Jerome says yoga might help Ginger control her mean streak, improve her slouch, and give her more grace.
3. Ginger suggests Jerome doesn't know anything about exercise.
4. Jerome says he always goes to her place.
5. a. It looks like a pigpen.
   b. It is full of clutter and dust, and Jerome never cleans up after himself.
6. Ginger hangs up on Jerome.
7. Answers will vary.

2 Changing the y to i

1. grouchier   grouchiest
2. rainier   rainiest
3. icier   iciest
4. stuffier   stuffiest
5. stretchier   stretchiest
6. rosier   rosiest

3 More Work with the Ending -y

chilly	bloody	1. hairy	6. brainy
hairy	jumpy	2. jumpy	7. salty
risky	salty	3. puffy	8. bloody
brainy	tricky	4. risky	9. tricky
puffy	greedy	5. chilly	10. greedy

4 Who Uses What?

1. iron
2. leash
3. spices
4. plow
5. sled
6. putty
7. globe
8. gloves
9. prop
10. brace

5 Compound Words

1. rail + road
2. basket + ball
3. under + ground
4. grand + mother
5. dream + land
6. grand + father
7. cheap + skate
8. sleep + over

Lesson 5

1 About the Story

1. It got you thinking about what kinds of information the story might contain.
2. She sang with a band, wrote songs, and gave voice lessons.
3. She had met Jerome six months ago in a hardware store.
4. Jerome worked as a clerk in the hardware store.
5. Ginger was in love with Jerome.
6. No one knows for sure how Jerome felt about Ginger.
7. Ginger's mother thought her daughter's apartment didn't look at all homey.
8. Ginger had not told her mother how wealthy she was.
9. Answers will vary.

2 The Ending -ly

lately	madly	1. properly	6. costly
truthfully	peacefully	2. shyly	7. lately
properly	wildly	3. truthfully	8. lively
oddly	costly	4. madly	9. peacefully
shyly	lively	5. wildly	10. Oddly

3 Words That Mean the Same

1. plead
2. brink
3. edgy
4. stir
5. shove
6. frighten
7. bright
8. gaze
9. beginning
10. dense
11. pledge
12. healthy

4 Compound Words

1. tooth + brush
2. Thanks + giving
3. over + board
4. gum + drop
5. flower + pot
6. back + ground
7. snow + ball
8. sea + weed
9. high + way
10. cross + walk

Lesson 6

1 About the Story

1. This story takes place in the hardware store.
2. It is evening.
3. a. Ginger might stop being angry with him.
   b. It might encourage her to paint her apartment.
4. The lid came off, and paint spilled all over Jerome, the counter, and the floor.
5. Tony laughed very hard.
6. It took seven hours to clean up the mess.
7. Answers may vary. The first paragraph of the story suggests that Jerome wants to take the paint now and perhaps pay for it when he gets his next paycheck.
8. Answers may vary.

2 More Work with the Ending -ly

freshly	hourly	1. neatly	6. squarely
neatly	tightly	2. rarely	7. commonly
thickly	rarely	3. hourly	8. tightly
squarely	successfully	4. certainly	9. thickly
commonly	certainly	5. freshly	10. successfully

3 Word Opposites

1. hairy
2. costly
3. frozen
4. rarely
5. skinny
6. ugly
7. fake
8. tense
9. risky
10. clear
11. given
12. loose

4 Compound Words

1. dish + rag
2. finger + nail
3. tail + spin
4. any + more
5. over + done
6. drug + store
7. finger + print
8. bath + tub

Lesson 7

1 About the Story

1. Steven had a slight cold and wasn't feeling too well.
2. He was catching on to the yoga exercises quite quickly.
3. Holly asked Steven if he wanted to go out for a cup of coffee.
4. The sugar in them could make people grouchy, restless, fat, and unhealthy.
5. He apparently has decided not to order a brownie when he says, "Well, so much for double-chocolate brownies."
6. Steven learned that yoga is a whole way of life. He also learned that in becoming involved with yoga he had a lot more to think about than he imagined he would.
7. a. Steven's apartment
   b. the YMCA
   c. a coffee shop

2 The Endings -ful and -less

A. restless
   sugarless
   armful
   harmful
   stressful
   spotless
   peaceful
   tasteless

B. 1. stressful
   2. tasteless
   3. harmful
   4. armful
   5. peaceful
   6. restless
   7. spotless
   8. sugarless

3 Same or Opposite?

1. opposite
2. opposite
3. same
4. same
5. same
6. same
7. same
8. opposite
9. same
10. same
11. opposite
12. same

4 Compound Words

1. knock + out
2. ship + wreck
3. life + guard
4. match + book
5. light + house
6. door + knob
7. star + fish
8. come + back
9. eye + sight
10. knee + cap

Lesson 8

1 About the Story

1. This story takes place in Ginger's apartment.
2. It probably takes place in the morning since Ginger was fixing breakfast.
3. Gail wanted to stay at Ginger's for a day or two.
4. Gail goes to see her parents only when she wants money.
5. She had banged her head against the front door.
6. Ginger suggested that Gail ought to think about how she is treating her parents.
7. We know that Gail doesn't live with her parents because the story said she visited them only when she wanted money.
8. Probably most students will feel that Gail is not treating her parents very well and that she should be more considerate.

2 More Work with the Endings -ful and -less

A. countless
   watchful
   painless
   spoonful
   painful
   faithful
   joyful
   worthless
   homeless
   sunless

B. 1. homeless
   2. spoonful
   3. sunless
   4. faithful
   5. painful
   6. watchful
   7. joyful
   8. countless
   9. painless
   10. worthless

3 Same or Opposite?

1. opposite
2. same
3. same
4. same
5. opposite
6. opposite
7. same
8. opposite
9. same
10. opposite
11. opposite
12. same

4 Compound Words

1. coffeecake
2. newsstand
3. washcloth
4. meatballs
5. scoreboard
6. waistline
7. leapfrog
8. pitchfork
9. crybaby
10. kinfolks
11. cheapskate
12. spendthrift

Lesson 9

1 About the Story

1. Jerome was hoping Ginger would leave him a message.
2. They told him to tell Ginger he was sorry.
3. Jerome went online to order new books, because he had read everything on his bookshelf.
4. Jerome didn't know anyone named Holly, so he thought the card was a mistake.
5. Steven didn't give Jerome a chance to say no.
6. Jerome agreed that he'd been spending too much time by himself.
7. At the beginning of the story, Jerome wants to avoid his friends and stay at home. By the end of the story, he wants to go out, and he feels lucky to have a good friend like Steven.
8. He is too proud.
9. Answers will vary.

2 The Ending -en

1. frozen	5. broken	9. threaten
2. fallen	6. taken	10. loosen
3. sunken	7. weaken	11. moisten
4. forgotten	8. written	12. mistaken

3 Which Word Does Not Fit?

1. friend	5. beef	8. everything
2. ice cubes	6. speak	9. promise
3. raincoat	7. mailman	10. task
4. brownies		

Lesson 10

1 About the Story

1. a. Finding a parking place was difficult.
   b. The machines might not work properly.
   c. You have to be careful not to lose anything.
2. Holly was writing "Out of Order" signs for the machines that didn't work.
3. Holly had tried two washing machines.
4. a. The four quarters and two dimes ($1.20) she lost suggests she tried two machines — sixty cents in each machine.
   b. She was writing two "Out of Order" signs.
5. Since she had hung up on him, he felt she should phone him to apologize.
6. Jerome wants to see her, so he should call her.
7. Jerome wasn't taking any steps to get what he wanted.
8. Answers may vary.

2 More Work with the Ending -en

1. driven	5. bitten	9. given
2. fallen	6. eaten	10. ridden
3. shaken	7. spoken	11. deepen
4. straightened	8. beaten	12. rotten

3 Which Word Does Not Fit?

1. newspaper	5. pest	9. ivy
2. month	6. drum	10. season
3. deck	7. saucepan	11. whale
4. building	8. highway	12. Rome

4 Spelling Check

1. breakfast	5. doctor	8. mirror
2. alphabet	6. coffee	9. Swiss
3. mammal	7. wedding	10. thirteen
4. Christmas		

Lesson 11

1 About the Story

1. a. Ginger had had her cell phone shut off.
   b. She had gone camping.
2. She was daydreaming about never having to work again.
3. a. She is going to carry her cell phone everywhere.
   b. She is going to paint her walls.
   c. She is going to read all the newspapers she can find.
4. Life in the city feels safer than camping in the woods.
5. Ginger had gone camping to perk herself up after her trouble with Jerome. When she thought she heard a growling sound, she became scared and ran away as fast as she could.
6. Answers will vary.
7. Answers will vary.

2 Words That Begin with re-

1. react	6. recall
2. refuse	7. recover
3. remarks	8. repeat
4. respect	9. rejected, rejection
5. reveal	10. require

3 Words That Mean the Same

1. lousy	5. nervous	8. require
2. respond	6. faithful	9. recall
3. boast	7. juicy	10. mistaken
4. rejoice		

4 What Is Where?

A Laundromat	YMCA	A Diner
1. bleach	1. exercise bikes	1. grill
2. coin machines	2. pool	2. oven
3. dryers	3. yoga class	3. waitress

5 What Is Where?

A Circus	A Concert	A Baseball Game
1. clowns	1. drums	1. center field
2. dancing bears	2. flutes	2. pitchers
3. sideshows	3. stage	3. scoreboard

Lesson 12

1 About the Story

1. Steven bought a new video game system at the mall.
2. She thought they were meant for children, not adults.
3. a. You control the games by moving your body around.
   b. You can get a workout while you play.
4. He held the control and swung his arms like he was swinging a baseball bat.
5. She didn't like golf or baseball, and she didn't like losing to Steven.
6. Steven is clumsy. He trips and misses steps. Holly is a natural dancer. She performs every dance move with ease.
7. Possible answer: Holly wanted to keep playing because she was doing better than Steven. Steven wanted to stop because he wasn't a good dancer.

2 More Work with Words That Begin with re-

1. refund	5. refresh	9. recovered
2. remove	6. reduce	10. return
3. report	7. retired	11. retreat
4. repair	8. related	12. record

3 Compound Words

1. footprint	5. homesick	9. paperback
2. leftovers	6. daybreak	10. courtroom
3. eggshell	7. standstill	11. lukewarm
4. deadline	8. wastebasket	12. playground

4 Word Opposites

1. wilt	5. natural	8. arrived
2. excited	6. moldy	9. scratchy
3. repair	7. sulky	10. bulky
4. adult		

Lesson 13

1 About the Story

1. Jerome thought he and Ginger could work out their quarrel face to face.
2. Tony was supposed to convince Ginger to come to the party.
3. a. He bought bug spray to kill the cockroaches in the kitchen.
   b. He cleared the cobwebs from the ceiling.
   c. He scrubbed the carpet.
4. He burned her favorite hip-hop songs and some Cuban salsa music.
5. The thought that Ginger and Tony might be out on a date together made Jerome cringe.
6. Jerome was too much of a gentleman to kick out his guests.
7. Answers will vary.

2 Word Opposites

1. grungy	5. merge	8. quarrel
2. except	6. forgive	9. contain
3. plunge	7. gain	10. borrow
4. despair		

3 Which Word Fits Best?

1. hip-hop	5. talk into	9. stale
2. hand	6. lung	10. present
3. Boston	7. land	11. roar
4. coffeecake	8. steam	12. year

4 Consonants

1. gŭt • ter	5. căn • not	9. pĕp • per
2. măt • ter	6. cŭt • ting	10. slĭp • per
3. sŭm • mer	7. măm • mal	11. qŭar • rel
4. hăp • pen	8. rŏt • ten	12. gŏb • ble

Lesson 14

1 About the Story

1. Mrs. Darkpill spends most of her time spying on her neighbors. She hides behind the curtains and watches them. If they do anything wrong, she reports them to the police.
2. Mrs. Darkpill thought the tree had grown too high. She claimed it blocked out all the bright sunlight that used to reach her house.
3. She told the police that Tony ought to be arrested for harassing her children.
4. Tony got frightened that she would press false charges against him with the police.
5. Answers will vary.

2 The gh and ght Words

1. might, right
2. right
3. neighbor, sighed
4. ought, daughters
5. dough, rough, cough, tough
6. sleigh, height, eight, bright
7. enough

3 Same or Opposite

1. same	5. opposite	9. same
2. same	6. opposite	10. same
3. same	7. opposite	11. same
4. opposite	8. opposite	12. opposite

4 More Work with Double Consonants

1. hĭd • den	5. thĭn • ner	8. shăl • ler
2. clŭt • ter	6. hĭt • ter	9. trăp • per
3. bĭt • ten	7. hŏb • by	10. cŏm • mon
4. wrăp • per		

Lesson 15

1 About the Story

1. Tony and Ginger decided to stay indoors because a downpour started right when Ginger arrived at Tony's house.
2. Ginger had parked in front of Mrs. Darkpill's driveway.
3. Tony threatened to call the cops and have her charged with trespassing.
4. Tony told Mrs. Darkpill that she should go stand in the rain and cool off a bit.
5. Ginger really started to laugh at the claim that she and Tony were having an affair.
6. Ginger saw that Mrs. Darkpill was clearly disturbed and that things could get out of hand.
7. Answers will vary.
8. Answers will vary.

2 The *ea* and *ee* Words

1. yearly, clearly, dreary, cheery
2. weather, feathers, seed, sneeze
3. sneer, sweat, beaches, peaches
4. leaves, trees, sleeves, breeze
5. near, year, cheer, leap
6. reason, season, clear, least

3 Syllables

1. card • board	5. fair • ly	9. cob • web
2. clear • ly	6. up • roar	10. fair • ness
3. cheer • ful	7. floor • board	11. down • pour
4. dough • nut	8. stair • way	12. in • vite

4 More Work with Units

1. months	4. quarts	7. letters
2. hours	5. ounces	8. rooms
3. seconds	6. feet	9. states

Lesson 16

1 About the Story

1. a. peanut butter balls
   b. prune whip
   c. date-nut bread
2. Holly is writing a cookbook.
3. peanut butter balls
4. prune whip
5. He complains rather than taking action to make life better.
6. He is living by a set of outdated rules.
7. The bread was burned.
8. Answers may vary.
9. Answers may vary.

2 Sounds for ow

1. flowerpot	5. downstream	9. shower
2. bowling	6. brownie	10. grown-ups
3. towel rack	7. pillow	11. rowboat
4. bowl	8. elbow	12. cow

3 More Work with Syllables

1. yesterday	4. helicopter	7. tightly
2. automobiles	5. laundromat	8. neighborhood
3. Cinderella	6. recipe	

4 Brain Benders

1. true	5. false	8. false
2. false	6. true	9. true
3. true	7. false	10. false
4. false		

Lesson 17

1 About the Story

1. a. Tony's apartment

   b. a diner
   c. a men's clothing store
2. Mr. Dennis is Tony's boss.
3. Since Mr. Dennis answered the phone in an "extremely unfriendly voice," we can assume he was in a bad mood.
4. Tony tells Mr. Dennis that he is coming down with the flu.
5. He decides to check out the sale at a men's clothing store.
6. Mr. Dennis sees Tony at the store when he is supposed to be home sick.
7. Answers will vary.
8. Answers will vary.

2 More Work with the Sounds for *ow*

1. crowbar	5. slowpoke	9. pillowcase
2. landowner	6. townspeople	10. scarecrow
3. blowout	7. downpour	11. breakdown
4. snowplow	8. wildflowers	12. overflow

3 Which Word Does Not Fit?

1. peas	5. weak	9. nervous
2. unfriendly	6. rain	10. destroy
3. knees	7. shelter	11. conceal
4. purse	8. relax	12. mute

4 More Work with Syllables

1. con • fess	9. win • ner
2. booth	10. pay • day
3. ex • treme	11. home • sick
4. ex • treme • ly	12. rest • room
5. shop • per	13. o • ver • board
6. flu	14. un • friend • ly
7. six • teen	15. bas • ket • ball
8. yes • ter • day	

Lesson 18

1 About the Story

1. Steven thinks Jerome can't admit when he's made a mistake and take the initiative to straighten out things with Ginger.
2. Steven is trying to get Jerome to understand that he will have to take some action in order to get what he wants out of life.
3. Jerome thinks Ginger might have started the fight with Tony's neighbor just to get out of going to his party.
4. Jerome only complains and won't do anything to get back together with Ginger.
5. Jerome seems to decide Steven is right. Evidence of this is Jerome's deciding to call Ginger.

2 Short Stories

1. discussed, expands, disagreed, extra, convince
2. exceeding, exchanged, unfriendly, unfit, extra
3. exhausted, uncertain, unhealthy, expenses, income

3 Spelling Check

1. thumb
2. August
3. wallet
4. paycheck
5. potato
6. Cinderella
7. waltz
8. cheerleader

4 More Words That Begin with *-in.*

1. inhale
2. invent
3. inform
4. invade
5. invite
6. instruct
7. infect
8. inspire

Lesson 19

1 About the Story

1. Jerome decides to go see her rather than calling her.
2. Most of the story takes place at the uptown café where Ginger is singing.
3. Ginger is sitting next to the piano player when Jerome first sees her.
4. At first, Jerome tells Ginger he came to see her because he wanted to hear her sing "September Song."
5. Jerome makes a joke about her mean streak and yoga. Ginger thinks he just wants to repeat their fight.
6. Ginger touches Jerome gently on the cheek and goes to sing "September Song."
7. Answers will vary.

2 Twelve Questions

1. upstairs
2. indoors
3. upbeat
4. income
5. disposing
6. overdone
7. complaining
8. imposing
9. recovered
10. replying
11. conforming
12. confused

3 The Four Seasons

Spring
1. April Fool's Day
2. flowers blooming
3. March
4. spring training

Summer
1. August
2. beach
3. Fourth of July
4. hot weather

Autumn
1. falling leaves
2. Halloween
3. October
4. schools open

Winter
1. December
2. ice skating
3. New Year's Eve
4. snowstorms

4 The Months of the Year

1. January
2. December
3. October
4. November
5. February
6. December
7. July
8. June (or May)
9. September (or August)
10. Answers will vary.
11. March
12. June
13. September
14. December
15. Answers will vary.
16. Answers will vary.

Lesson 20

1 About the Story

1. Holly is giving a party to celebrate signing a contract for her cookbook.
2. Jerome asked Holly if she is serving health food or real food.
3. Holly is sick of all the health food she had to eat while testing recipes for her cookbook.
4. She wants to thank him for testing the recipes.
5. She serves prune whip as a gag.
6. The real dessert is chocolate cheesecake.
7. He thinks Holly and Steven will start dating.
8. Jerome thinks they'll be at the YMCA trying to stand on their heads.
9. Jerome seems to be happy and wants his friends to be happy too.
10. Answers will vary.

2 More Work with Compound Words

1. passport
2. heartbreak
3. homebody
4. sundown
5. backbone
6. firecracker
7. bedtime
8. poorhouse
9. homeland
10. slowpoke

3 Words That Mean the Same

1. find
2. tired
3. overweight
4. hardly
5. hurled
6. rough
7. upscale
8. cold
9. joking
10. pout

4 Word Opposites

1. female
2. sour
3. past
4. shame
5. freeze
6. heal
7. deny
8. flushed
9. certain
10. contract

5 Feelings

1. relaxed. Holly practices yoga because it calms her down and makes her feel good.
2. excited. At last, Joan can try to get the job of her dreams.
3. angry. He had gotten nothing for his dollar.
4. overcome with feeling. Charles cried because he was so happy that he won.
5. rejected. John felt his neighbor didn't want him at the party.
6. thrilled. Ted didn't like his boss, and soon his boss would be leaving.
7. thankful. She felt very grateful that her son was safe.
8. Answers will vary.

Review: Lessons 1–20

1 Word Study

1. c	6. b	11. d
2. b	7. a	12. a
3. d	8. c	13. a
4. a	9. a	14. c
5. b	10. c	15. d

2 Words That Mean the Same

1. limit	5. poor	8. hurry
2. want	6. content	9. grab
3. fussy	7. hoist	10. staff
4. fib		

3 Word Opposites

1. straight	5. underneath	8. loosen
2. spotless	6. fancy	9. lying
3. shrink	7. happiness	10. costly
4. quiet		

4 Syllables

1. cloud • less	6. thought • ful
2. suc • cess • ful	7. re • tire
3. rob • ber	8. hand • shake
4. side • ways	9. pro • tein
5. thir • teen	10. peace • ful • ly

5 Word Sounds

1. walk	4. great	7. could
2. city	5. good	8. certain
3. gentle	6. plow	

6 Spelling Check

1. courtroom	5. school	8. ashtray
2. highway	6. eyesight	9. kitchen
3. England	7. cookbook	10. exhaust
4. eggshell		

Answer: cheesecake